THE SUNNY SIDE
OF CRAZY

Patricia Mikouchi

The Sunny Side of Crazy

Copyright 2022 by Patricia Mikouchi
ISBN 978-0-578-98029-4 (Paperback)
    978-0-5-7898030-0 (Ebook)
Cover Design by Kindamohamed at Fiverr
Book Formatted by Asfahimbd at Fiverr

Narrative Non-fiction, Inspirational, Family, Psychology. Cultural/Social Issues, Mental Health

Printed and distributed by IngramSpark
Website: https://TheSunnySideofCrazy.com

AUTHOR'S NOTE:

Crazy is a five-letter word with many meanings and Mikala has heard them all. In fact, she would be the first to tell you her secret friend Sam was crazy in love with mom, Suki was crazy about teaching, and Calle was crazy silly. Skye was crazy sexy and Tin, well, he was always crazy angry. But Mikala's not and never was crazy. She was different. She had a disorder. To those who find the use of "Crazy" politically incorrect, insensitive, or not a literal enough word, Mikala would say, "My life was crazy at times. Still, most of the time it was filled with sunshine."

DEDICATED

To my family for their patience and support

To my friends for their inspiration and encouragement

And, in memory of my muse lost to Covid.

Thank you!

CONTENTS

The Sunny Side of Crazy

Part 3

Hidden Dangers

INTRODUCTION

The world over, many mothers have wondered:

Does my child have imaginary friends,?

Why does my child behave this way?

Will they outgrow their odd behavior?

Is my child normal?

How do I know?

Who can I ask?

Often, their concern passes as quickly as their child's behavior. But, what if it doesn't? What if the odd behavior continues and begins to affect the child's health and relationships?

The Sunny Side of Crazy was inspired by a story of a little girl with big secrets and odd behaviors, and her Mother's attempt to understand her.

It is the story of how one therapist is able to unlock a young woman's secrets and offer her a path to a normal future. But that future comes at a price she might not be willing to pay.

THE CRACKED POT

A water bearer in China had two large pots, each hung on the ends of a pole that he carried across his neck. One pot had a crack in it, while the other pot was perfect and always delivered a full portion of water.

At the end of the long walk from the stream to the house, the cracked pot arrived only half full.

For a full two years, this went on daily, with the water bearer delivering only one and a half pots full of water to his house.

Of course, the perfect pot was proud of its accomplishments, perfect for which it was made.

But, the poor cracked pot was ashamed of its own imperfection and miserable that it was able to accomplish only half of what it had been made to do.

After two years of what it perceived to be a bitter failure, it spoke to the water bearer one day by the stream....

"I am ashamed of myself because this crack in my side causes water to leak out all the way back to your house."

The Sunny Side of Crazy

The bearer said to the pot," Did you notice that there were flowers only on your side of the path but not on the other pot's side?"

That's because 1 have always known about your flaw, and 1 planted flower seeds on your side of the path. Every day while we walk back you've watered them. For two years, 1 have been able to pick these beautiful flowers to decorate the table. Without you being just the way you are, there would not be this beauty to grace the house."

Author unknown

PART 1
In the Beginning

CHAPTER 1
A WOUNDED HEART

Five-year-old Michiko thought it was going to be the best day of her life. It wasn't. It was one of the worst.

From the moment she woke up, she knew the day was going to be special. Her mother let her sleep in. "No nursery school today," she said as Michiko climbed out of bed. Instead of her dreary school uniform, her mother allowed her to put on her favorite bright yellow sweatpants and a Mickey Mouse shirt. Just looking at those cheerful colors made her happy. That was the artist in her, the brighter the colors, the happier she felt.

If that weren't enough, wherever they were going, Grandmother was going with them. When Grandmother was around, Michiko felt warm, safe, and loved. Her mother would never raise her voice in front of her grandmother. In fact, she didn't remember her mother speaking to Grandmother much at all. *No matter, she thought, for sure, it was going to be an extra special day.* Even the gloomy sky, howling wind, and falling rain outside her window couldn't dampen her spirit. Mother grabbed a hairbrush and quickly ran it through Michiko's long silky hair.

Suddenly, Papa's face burst into the room. Michiko shivered as he stared at her for a long moment and then roared, "For God's sake, how long does it take to brush a child's hair? Your taxi is waiting."

The Sunny Side of Crazy

"Come on, Michiko, you know Grandmother hates being late," her mother said nervously. Michiko smiled as she remembered Grandmother would be joining them. That was all that mattered. The day couldn't start any better. It had to be an awesome day!

By the time they joined Grandmother in the taxi, the rain had turned into a heavy downpour, common to the muggy Japanese rainy season. As she struggled to close her little red umbrella, Grandmother leaned over and closed it for her. She snuggled closer to Grandmother, expecting to be told how pretty she looked, or at least greeted by her usual "Good morning how's my little Michiko-chan?"

Instead, her Grandmother looked at her sadly, gently touched her cheek, and barked at her mother, "We're late again. I hope Miss Sarah waits for us." *Miss who? Miss Sarah? What a funny name,* she thought. *Why would a foreigner be waiting for us?*

Then, she noticed Grandmother was wearing her nicest kimono, which she wore only for the most special of occasions. Grandmother must have thought it would be a special day, too.

Twenty minutes later, their taxi pulled in front of a brightly lit coffee shop. By then, the sky had turned black and thunder roared. Michiko opened her umbrella again, grabbed her grandmother's sleeve, and followed her into the cheerful little coffee shop. It was called Dunkin Donuts, one of the many new foreign shops lining the streets of Osaka.

The smell of hot coffee and warm donuts filled ever inch of the room, and she suddenly recalled being there before. Grandmother brought her here a long time ago, for her fifth birthday. They'd laughed as they shared a huge chocolate donut followed by her favorite — a strawberry one. Now, it seemed like that was a long time ago.

"*Irrashaimase* ! Welcome to Dunkin Donuts !" called out the cheerful young clerk from behind the counter. She looked directly at Michiko, "What would you like this morning, little lady?"

How could she possibly choose? It didn't matter. Her mother immediately replied, "Just two coffees and a plain donut for the child, please. " As her mother waited, Grandmother gently took Michiko by the hand and led her toward a booth where a foreign lady was sitting. It was the first time she'd seen a foreigner closeup, and what she saw frightened her. The foreigner's hair and eyes were so light they appeared colorless, like a dead Japanese. She immediately sensed danger and hid behind Grandmother. "Here, sit next to me," Grandmother said, as she pulled Michiko forward, picked her up, and slid her into the booth. Moments later, her mother followed, briefly bowed to the foreigner and sat down.

Grandmother was the first to speak." Thank you for coming Miss. Sarah," she said. We think it's time for the child to leave. We can't wait any longer. My daughter is pregnant again, and the baby will be coming soon. This child needs to be living in another home."

This child? What child? Wait! A sickening fear overcame Michiko. She *wondered if she could be the child they were talking about? Leave? Leave where? Go where? She struggled to focus. What was she hearing? How could that be?*

The Sunny Side of Crazy

As loudly and clearly as if he were standing next to her, Michiko heard Papa's voice repeat the words he'd spoken many times before: "You're a bad girl Michiko, you're a bad, bad girl."

Her mind raced. *Was she being sent away because she was a bad, bad girl? Was she not good enough for her family*

She slid down in the booth and turned her attention to a table nearby. A little girl her same age was giggling and wiggling as she tried to push a doughnut between her mother's tightly closed lips. When her mother finally opened her mouth, the little girl slipped, and milk quickly flowed over the table and down to the floor.

Michiko froze. Her heart beat faster. She held her breath, sat up straight, and stared directly at her donut. *One second, two seconds, three seconds, four, breathe.* The little girl began crying but her father started laughing. Michiko couldn't believe it! Soon the little girl's mother joined the laughter. Mopping up the mess and gently drying her daughter's tears "Satoko, it's okay! But, you do this every time we go out. You need to be more careful." Her parents continued to hug her and laugh.

Michiko closed her eyes and let her mind wander. For a brief moment, she dreamed of being that little girl, felt that mother's arms around her as she promised everything was going to be okay.

No! She was bad, and bad girls don't deserve families like that. She hugged herself tightly and began to rock back and forth.

The Sunny Side of Crazy

The foreigner's voice interrupted her thoughts, and with a jolt, she was back, still confused and worried. She looked across the table and studied the woman sitting next to her mother. She spoke Japanese fluently but looked dead, like the ghosts in her storybooks. She decided she didn't like those storybooks, ghosts, or this foreigner.

Finally, her mother spoke in barely more than a whisper, "My husband will not raise Michiko any longer; she's not his child."

Then whose child was she? What did that mean? She felt like crying but held back her tears. Crying would make no difference. It wouldn't change anything. She had stopped crying long ago. Then, the woman spoke again, and this time her words were terrifying " I know someone in America who would be a wonderful mother."

Another mother? Did she hear that correctly? Another mother? Another country? A country where everyone would be colorless and speak words she couldn't understand? Would she have a foreigner for a mother? That couldn't be! She was Japanese! She wouldn't be herself anymore.

Nothing made sense. Where was she going? What would happen to her? Was she going to a country called America? Thoughts and voices intruded. Whose thoughts?

Whose voices? She didn't know.

"I don't want to be here. I wish I weren't me. I want to disappear. I want to melt away!"

"You can't."

"Why not?"

"You need to stay. You need to hear this; you need to know."

"You'll be okay, Michiko."

Okay? That would not be possible. How could she be okay? Wasn't she there to be given away?

The foreigner looked at her mother, "You need to decide what you're going to do."

Her mother didn't say anything. She never did. Not when she should have, like when Michiko walked to nursery school in the rain, and Papa drove right past her. Or, when she was left alone in the bath with Papa while her Mother put her little brother Takashi to bed.

Miss Sarah reached for her raincoat. Michiko waited. *Mother had to say something. She was her Mother! She couldn't give her away!* She'd be good if she could stay.

But, as if reading Michiko's mind, her grandmother quickly said, "Michiko needs to go. She needs a new family, and she will be better off in America."

And her mother?

Her mother said nothing at all.

CHAPTER 2
SARAH'S HOME

A day later, the rain stopped, the sun came out and Michiko awoke to loud knocking at the front door. She made her way to the window, peeked out, and knew for sure that the foreign ghost lady was more than a bad dream.

She bolted for her hiding place in the back of the closet just beyond the sliding doors, but Grandmother hadn't put the futons away and there weren't any to hide behind! She huddled down in the corner.

"Michiko, I know you are in there. You must come out now. It's time to go." Her grandmother's voice sounded strange, cold, distant, strained. Michiko stood up and made her way out. For the first time, she saw tears in her grandmother's eyes.

She silently obeyed and followed her grandmother down the stairs. Grandmother handed her a present, a new red Mickey Mouse bag containing three pairs of panties, one pair of pajamas with bunnies hopping around the front, and two sets of shorts with matching tops.

Then, her grandmother said what she was to hear over and over again, first in Japanese, later in English, "Shikata ga nai; dai joubu. It can't be helped; everything will be okay."

But, it wasn't okay, and it wouldn't be for a very long time.

Her grandmother opened the door, bowed to Miss Sarah put her hand on Michiko's shoulder and gently nudged her through the door. She turned around, walked inside, and Michiko never saw her again.

Bewildered and afraid, Michiko let the ghost lady take her hand. An hour later they arrived at Sarah's Home, a temporary residence for children waiting for foreign adoptions. Among them were five babies, four toddlers, and Miss. Sarah's seven adopted children,

Michiko tightened her grip on Miss Sarah's hand as they stepped into the big western-style house. The entrance looked like other Japanese entrances, except instead of a wall cabinet filled with neatly placed shoes, this one was empty. Mismatched shoes of various sizes and colors were scattered all over the floor. Michiko slipped out of her shoes and put them inside the cabinet before slipping into the pair of oversized slippers.

Within seconds, the smell of strange food combined with the sound of children laughing and babies crying overwhelmed her. *I don't belong here.* This was the last thought she had before a seizure overcame her.

The next morning she woke to the familiar smell of Japanese rice and miso, as well as the smiling face of Hannah, one of Sarah's adopted daughters.

"Don't worry Michiko, I promise I'm going to take very good care of you," Hannah said in perfect Japanese.

Michiko stared at her. She wanted to go home, play with her little brother, help grandmother cook. She longed to sleep in her scary old bed, but her family didn't want her anymore. She wondered if Papa had told Sarah what a bad girl she was. Maybe Hannah didn't know yet.

The Sunny Side of Crazy

Hannah kept her promise and treated Michiko as a precious little sister. Days turned into weeks and weeks into months. One of the younger children and two of the infants left. She wasn't sure where they went, but Hannah said they went to live with "forever families" in America. "Someday," she said, "you'll have a forever family too, and Michiko, forever mothers never give their children away."

Michiko didn't want to hear that and thought *maybe, just maybe, if she was good enough, Sarah would let her stay. Then, she could visit Grandmother and Takashi and still be close to Hannah.* She trusted Hannah, and sometimes when she was tired and scared, she would reach for Hannah's breast. Hannah would gently remove her hand and say, "No, Michiko, I'm not your mother; I'm your friend." Hannah became Michiko's first real friend.

The Sunny Side of Crazy

CHAPTER 3
THROUGH A MOTHER'S EYES

The call came in the middle of the night. Reluctantly, I pulled myself from the comfort of my bed and headed to the kitchen. I had to answer. A call that came that late was always important and unfortunately, usually bad news. "Your sister's died in an accident; Your brother didn't make it; and the most recent call, "Dad just died of a heart attack."

I paused, took a deep breath, and reached for the phone. I braced myself, picked up the receiver, and put it to my ear.

" Anna, I'm sorry to call you so late but I need to ask you something important."

I recognized the Southern drawl immediately!

"Sarah? What a surprise! How are you? "

"I'm fine. I just wanted to tell you I have a little girl who needs a mother. I've been praying about it, and your name keeps coming to mind. I know it's been a long time since we talked, but when you lived here, you told me you'd love to have another daughter. Would you consider becoming her adoptive mother?"

It had been almost twenty years since I'd last talked to Sarah. Now, an empty nester, about to celebrate by buying a horse, I stood there in shock. Twenty years, and my life had changed, but not my love for little girls. Nor had my tendency to make impulsive decisions. Ebony, the horse didn't stand a chance.

I returned to bed that night with a head full of questions, Sarah wanted me to sleep on it, but we both knew the decision had already been made. I gave up trying to sleep and went into the kitchen, pen, and paper in hand and thought about all I'd heard.

"She's a beautiful child, healthy, but with the possibility of epilepsy. She's quiet. She won't speak to anyone but my fourteen-year-old daughter, Hannah. Maybe the best way to describe her would be to say she's cautious and curious."

"Sarah, what about her family?"

" Well, we never know everything, but her father claims she isn't his child and refuses to raise her. The girl's mother is pregnant again and has decided to give this child up. It was the child's grandmother who contacted me. She seems to be the only family member truly looking out for the child's welfare. I don't know much more than that."

" I've never forgotten how often you talked about wanting another daughter, and I know it's been a long time, but I thought I'd call to see if you still felt that way."

A while? *That was about 20 years ago! But then, that was Sarah. Time wasn't important to her.*

Sarah was one of many missionaries who, following World War 11, responded to General MacArthur's call for Christianity to fill the void left by the Emperor's renunciation of divinity. Many missionaries responded and returned home discouraged by the Buddhist and Shinto hold on society. They found conversion far more difficult than they had ever imagined.

The Sunny Side of Crazy

But not Sarah. She took her time and found a way to work within a very complicated system. With the help of her Baptist church and compassionate doctors, Sarah founded her home for abandoned children. She moved mountains to match children with forever families and each placement was a miracle. Now, I was about to receive one of my own.

It was almost morning when I fell asleep marveling at how my years in Japan, and unlikely friendship with a missionary had brought about this special event.

In saying yes, I was swamped with paperwork, all of which had to be translated before being sent to numerous agencies. Sarah kept me up to date with progress on the Japanese side, and I worked on everything else. The process moved along smoothly as if it was meant to be. Since the Japanese are extremely concerned about the welfare of adopted children, I expected delays, but Sarah kept the faith, and we never incurred a problem.

All I needed to finalize the adoption was an excellent home inspection. I cleaned and cleaned, then cleaned some more. Surprisingly, the agency's social worker hardly seemed to notice how my house shined. He asked to see the child's room, and then asked a series of questions about why I wanted to adopt, what my financial situation was and what my plans were for child care.

When he left, he said I'd have a report within the week, and in his opinion, it would be an excellent placement. As promised, the report arrived a few days later and I immediately purchased one round trip and one one-way ticket to a whole new adventure.

The Sunny Side of Crazy

CHAPTER 4
NO TURNING BACK

As the days passed, Michiko began to feel safer and a little happier, however, just as she thought Miss Sarah would keep her, Hannah brought her a letter from her new forever mother. Miss Sarah translated it.

Dear Mikala,

I'm so happy I'm going to be your new mother. I thought you would like to know a little about your new home. You will have a pretty bedroom upstairs. I hope you like pink because it's pink with cute pictures of kittens on the walls. Sarah told me you love them. We don't have kittens, but we have two cute puppies, Rambo and Rebel. They might bark the first time they meet you, but they would never hurt you.

There are Japanese paintings in many rooms and a small Japanese lantern in the garden. I hope this will help you feel at home.

Did Miss Sarah tell you that you have an older sister? She works for Japan Airlines and will visit you sometime next week. You will not have a father here, but you will have a happy family. Here's a picture of our family and our puppies.

I love you Miki, and I can't wait to meet you.

Your New Mommy

After reading the letter, Miss Sarah left to check on the babies, and Hannah sat next to Michiko patiently reading the letter again, trying to make it sound more appealing. Usually, Michiko loved listening to Hannah read, but not this time. She only had one question.

"Who's Miki ?"

"Well little Michiko, you will be living in America so you will have an American name. Your new mother is going to name you Mikala, and in America, people use nicknames. Mikala would be too long so they will just call you Miki."

Michiko stared at Hannah

"LIKE the MOUSE ?"

Hannah burst out laughing when she realized the only Miki Michiko had ever heard of was Micky Mouse.

"No, little Michiko, she said, Miki isn't just a mouse. It's a name for pretty little girls like you, Michiko, you will always share your Japanese name with Princess Michiko of Japan, but in America, people will call you Micky."

Michiko snuggled closer to Hannah and didn't say another word.

Sure enough, a week later her new sister arrived and Michiko hid behind the sofa. At first, she couldn't believe this woman could be her new sister. She was too old to be a sister, and she looked and spoke like a Japanese person. Hannah explained that her father was Japanese but not her mother. An hour later, Hannah crawled behind the sofa and sat down next to Michiko. "Michiko, your sister came a long, long way to meet you. You need to be polite. Come, let's go out together." She took Michiko's hand and led her out of hiding.

"Hello Michiko, I am so glad you've come out to see me. I've wanted to meet you for a long time. Now you're here, and I'm very happy to see you.

Michiko watched her but never said a word. She didn't know what to say. *She thought her big sister came to see if she was good enough to be her little sister.*

Shortly after the visit, something terrible happened. Miss Sarah took Michiko back to her Japanese mother's home. Michiko couldn't understand why. *Was she going to stay there? What had she done?* Over and over Miss Sarah said, " Michiko, you're a very good girl; you've done nothing wrong, but I must have some important papers signed. Until Papa signs them, you may have to stay with your family."

So, back she went. There, she saw Takashi's new baby sister _____ a very pretty baby adored by Mother and Papa. At first, she wondered if she'd been replaced by one of Sarah's babies so she looked the baby over carefully. No, this baby wasn't one of Sara's, and besides, Papa said this baby was his real daughter,

Michiko wanted to ask Grandmother if the baby was a good one, but Grandmother wasn't home and Papa signed the papers so quickly they were back at Sarah's home in time for dinner

Now, Takashi had a new sister, Grandmother had a new little lady, and Sarah had her papers.

Although Michiko was still five, she knew she was about to lose everything she had ever known family, county, even her name. She wondered what was next. It didn't take long to find out.

On Mother's Day, Michiko woke up to Hannah singing, "Michiko, it's time to wake up. You're going to meet your new mother today! Tomorrow, you're going to America."

What? No, she wasn't ready! She wanted to stay. There she knew what to expect. She'd miss the big house, helping Hannah take care of the babies, and even sitting at the large dining table where one by one each of the older children told God what they were thankful for. Michiko never said anything.

Now she was terrified. She'd have to go with a foreigner to another country where she would be far away from everything and everyone. Her new mother probably would not speak Japanese.

It was better to feel nothing than to feel a breaking heart. She shut down, became quiet, and was silent as Hannah packed underwear, shorts, tops, and new pajamas in Michiko's Micky Mouse bag. Once packed, Hannah smiled and handed her a little box with a red bow on top.

"Go ahead, open it," she said.

Michiko slowly untied the bow and looked at the little silver bracelet inside.

"It matches mine, Michiko. It's a friendship bracelet and it means we'll be friends forever. Aren't you going to say thank you?"

Michiko stared at Hannah blankly in silence. It would be a long time before she would ever speak again.

The Sunny Side of Crazy

"Come on, Honey, we have to go downstairs now."

Hannah looked at Michiko sadly and put the present in her bag.

An hour later, Miss Sarah, Hannah, and Michiko climbed out of a taxi in front of Osaka train station. While Miss Sarah bought tickets, Hannah and Michiko began the long climb up to the platform. *How many stairs? One, two, three, four, five, briefly losing count, she remembered, oh yes, she was five. She wondered when she would be six? Six, seven, eight stairs behind and way too many ahead to count.*

Well, she thought, *I can draw lots of stairs on my maps.* Michiko planned to draw many maps, ones that would bring her back to Osaka. Someday, she thought, *I'll come back and see Takashi and Grandma and maybe even the baby that replaced me. I'll need good maps to find my way back.*

The roar of the approaching bullet train interrupted her thoughts. Takashi and Michiko had long wanted to ride on one of these slick new trains, but today, it was the last thing Michiko wanted to do. There would be no turning back. She was supposed to meet her new mother at a famous hotel in the middle of Tokyo. But when they arrived, none of the foreign faces belonged to her new mother.

In addition to a missing mother, Miss Sarah had forgotten Michiko's passport back in Osaka. Sarah sent Hannah back to look for it and of course, Michiko hoped Hannah wouldn't be able to find it and she was disappointed that Miss Sarah didn't look worried.

Sarah leaned over and Michiko heard the words she was beginning to hate. "It can't be helped. Don't worry; everything's going to be okay."

Suddenly, a voice came over the loudspeaker, first in Japanese and then in English. "A phone call for Miss Sarah. Miss Sarah, you have a phone call, please come to the front desk."

Sarah returned a few minutes later with a smile covering her entire face. Michiko's new mother would arrive shortly.

Minutes later Michiko saw a lady peeking in, and tapping on the huge glass window next to her. For a brief moment, the two of them made eye contact. It only lasted a second and was the last eye contact they were to have for months.

A moment later, Michiko's new mother was right in front of her, leaning down to hug her. Michiko quickly sidestepped the hug, darted behind a potted plant, and stared past the new foreign ghost lady.

"She doesn't know me! And, if she did, she probably wouldn't want to hug me anyway," Michiko thought.

Miss Sarah and Michiko's new mom hugged, laughed, talked, and hugged some more. Michiko couldn't understand a word they said, but it didn't matter, foreign faces said it all. Unlike Japanese faces, foreign faces seemed to be talking all the time.

When they moved to the hotel dining room, Hannah came flying through the door waving something small in her hand. "Mom, I found it. Her passport, I've got it."

Michiko's heart sank. She now knew for sure she wouldn't be going back to Sarah's. Her small glimmer of hope vanished. *She briefly wondered if she would ever really come back. What if? What if? What if? She had to go to America now, but she believed she would return someday.*

Her head began to hurt. Inside her head, a conversation began:

"Am I really going away?"

"Of course you are, you bad, stupid girl!"

"I don't want to go."

"So, no one cares."

"Can't do anything about it anyway, can you?"

"Don't worry, we'll be with you"

"I want to go back home!"

"You don't have one, remember?"

The elevator doors closed on Hannah and Sarah's smiling faces. A loud bing sounded as Michiko and her new mother passed all but the fourth floor. In Japan, the fourth floor can be considered unlucky, so some hotels skip it altogether. They stepped off on the "lucky fifth" and entered a room at the far end of the hall, When Michiko's mother opened the door, Mikala noticed a pile of new clothes, coloring books, puzzles, and snacks, and a baby doll sitting on the desk but her eyes quickly moved to and settled on the stuffed white rabbit sitting in the chair next to it.

The Sunny Side of Crazy

Michiko's new mother stooped down and said in the strangest sounding Japanese, "It's late and our airplane leaves early in the morning, so I'll help you get ready for bed. Is that okay?"

Michiko backed away, picked up her little red Micky Mouse bag, and walked into the bathroom. The lock clicked and her mother listened, half amused and half-concerned. The little girl pottied, brushed her teeth, ran water in the sink, and reappeared in her bunny pajamas. She walked directly to the white rabbit, picked it up, and climb into bed.

All the while the little girl ignored her new mother. Finally, she closed her eyes and pretended not to hear her mother say, "O ya sami na sai, little Michiko, good night."

By six a.m. Michiko and her mother were in one of the largest airports in the world. For Michiko, it was terrifying! Bright lights, loud noises, big people speaking strange languages, and everyone pushing carts big enough to run her over.

At first, she let her new mother hold her hand; she didn't even try to pull away. The foreigners all looked alike, and she wasn't sure she could find her new mother if she got lost.

But, then she heard the one English word she recognized repeating over and over, Michigan, Michigan, blah, blah, blah, Michigan. Suddenly, she didn't care if she got lost. Getting lost had to be better than going wherever with this strange woman. Still holding her mother's hand, she let herself be guided into the closest bathroom.

The Sunny Side of Crazy

"Michiko, you need to use the bathroom before we get on the plane." For the first time, her mother let go of her hand. Michiko pottied and switched places. Decision made! *She wasn't going,* She slipped behind the cart and outside the door. Before her mother could stand up, she was down the escalator, and around the corner. She stopped suddenly to look at a beautiful bright kimono in a nearby gift shop. *Hadn't she'd seen it before? Hadn't they just been there? Wasn't she in that shop? Was she going the wrong way?* She turned back toward the escalator and started to run, but it was too late. One of the biggest, scariest policemen she'd ever seen stepped directly in front of her. She froze.

He stooped down.

"Where do you think you are going, little lady? Are you lost?"

She was about to say, no, when she heard her new mother screaming.

"Michiko, where are you? Michiko, Doko desu ka, Michiko?"

Her new mother ran up, scooped Michiko up, and quickly deposited her in the luggage cart she was dragging behind her.

The policeman put his hand firmly on the cart and gave her mother a stern look. Before he could say a word, she was pulling passports and adoption paper from her luggage. Meanwhile, a crowd of curious bypassers gathered around. Some were grumbling, others gawking but most were laughing. Michiko watched her new mother's face turn from white to pink to bright red as she tried to explain how she'd lost her new little daughter in the bathroom.

The officer inspected the papers slowly and carefully as her mother pleaded with him,

"Please hurry! our flight is leaving! "

Finally, he handed the papers back and broke into an amused grin. He took Michiko from the cart, waved the crowd aside, and led the way into a plane filled with clapping passengers. He put Michiko in her seat, the luggage in an overhead bin, and bowed before leaving the plane. Embarrassed by the cheering, Michiko's mother bowed to the clapping passengers, buckled her daughter into the window seat, set the white rabbit in the middle, and quickly slid as far down into her seat as possible. She was exhausted and looking forward to using the fourteen hours ahead to get acquainted with her new daughter.

There was no way of knowing what the child was thinking because Michiko simply sat staring out the window as Japan became smaller and smaller, finally disappearing from sight.. Michiko then turned, pulled paper and crayons from her Mickey Mouse bag, and began drawing maps. Maps from her family's home to Sarah's, from Sarah's to the train station, and from the train station to the airport. Finally, three dots, a large one with an arrow to a smaller one with another arrow through squiggly water lines to nowhere.

Then, she carefully folded her maps and tucked them into the bottom of her Mickey Mouse bag, turned her attention to the puzzles, coloring books, and White rabbit, all the while ignoring the woman watching her.

The Sunny Side of Crazy

Michiko's mother watched wondering how to begin bonding. It occurred to her that with all the excitement, paperwork, travel plans, and hours of preparation, she'd spent little time thinking about what might be going on in this little girl's head.

"Don't worry, everything is going to be okay," she said in her rusty Japanese. That was true, because, for this little girl, things couldn't get any worse.

Every gesture she made was ignored. She tried talking to Michiko, but she might as well have been talking to the wind. She received no response. She tried coloring with her, and the coloring book closed on her hand. Finally, when the lights dimmed and passengers became quiet, she raised the armrests, put a pillow on her lap, and made a soft little bed for Michiko. She gently laid Michiko down across the seats.

That lasted less than a minute. Michiko promptly stood up, moved the pillow closer to the window, and climbed back up. She covered herself and slept with her feet on her mother's lap for the next four hours. Her mother resisted the urge to laugh. At last, she was seeing some emotion and she told herself she would probably do the same thing if she were Michiko.

Hours later, when a flight attendant brought breakfast, Michiko's mother realized she was not the only one Michiko was avoiding eye contact with. Michiko accepted her meals and nodded in response to questions but focused her eyes on anything but people. It happened with whoever tried to speak with her. Before the end of the flight, her mother had began gently cupping Michiko's face in her hands and turning it

29

toward whoever was speaking. That continued long after they arrived in America.

Time passed slowly but the hours of cartoons, barely edible food, and patches of sleep finally ended. Michiko and her mother listened as the pilot's words came over the loudspeaker.

"We will soon be descending in Detroit, Michigan, please put your trays up and your seat in an upright position. Thank you for flying with us and have a great day."

That was the day Michiko left Japan, and Mikala arrived in America.

CHAPTER 5
THROUGH A MOTHER'S EYES

The Challenges started immediately after arriving home. It was clear Mikala didn't want, nor had any intention, of having anything to do with me.

I always believed if you gave a child enough love, they would love you back. It didn't take long to find out how naive I was. Days and nights were exhausting and frustrating.

I was filled with self-doubt and despair. Mikala kept as much space as possible between us. If I got too close, she'd back away and stare at me. I wanted to know what was going on behind her beautiful almond eyes. At the same time, I was afraid. Afraid I might find nothing but pure anger and hurt. It was devastating!

I'd found a daycare close to my office and dreamed of mommy/daughter lunchtimes. That's what it remained, a dream. When I walked in at noon, she walked away as if she didn't know me.

The truth was, she ignored everyone except Adam. Adam was different. His dark skin and hair may have reminded her of her brother back in Japan. Whatever the reason, I was happy she was not entirely alone. The other children ignored her, just as she ignored them.

One day the director pulled me aside and said, "I suppose you know something isn't right with Mikala. She won't talk to anyone, parallel plays, and lags behind other children her age."

I was speechless and worried. Was I making too many excuses? Was I in total denial?

She was given away by her parents, adopted by a strange-looking lady, taken to an unfamiliar country where people spoke an odd language. Wasn't that reason enough to lag behind?

"I suggest you put her in therapy as soon as possible."

Sure, I thought. *Does she really think a Japanese-speaking therapist exists anywhere around here?*

When I returned home, I pulled Mikala's pre-adoption physical form from the file. This is what it said

PRE-ADOPTION HEALTH REPORT FOR MICHIKO YAMADA

Health Report;   Michiko is a five-year-old girl approved for foreign adoption.

She has no communicable disease and her health is acceptable. The adoptive parent should be informed of the following:

Michiko shows signs of nutritional deficiency and failure to thrive. She is below average in weight and height and may suffer from epileptic seizures. Michiko should have immediate dental care to address bottle rot. Her hearing and eyesight are excellent, but she shows little interest in her surroundings. She refused to speak during her examination. We would recommend a full psychological assessment and follow-up as required.

The Sunny Side of Crazy

Wow, not exactly a clean bill of health! So, therapy had been suggested before her adoption. Had I forgotten? Denial can be so persuasive.

That night, I watched her prepare for bed and could no longer deny her bedtime ritual was abnormal. I'd fix her a bubble bath, and she'd wait for me to leave. If I left the door open more than the slightest crack, she'd walk over and close it in my face. I'd hold the handle to disable the lock and listen while she undressed, put her clothes on the back of the toilet, bathed, dried herself, and brushed her teeth. Then, she'd come out and climb in bed with White Rabbit. It was like watching a little robot and would have been funny if it weren't so sad.

Looking at Mikala, most people would see a beautiful little girl with enormous almond eyes. Perhaps they would think she was a little shy but sweet, polite, and well-behaved. The truth was, she was becoming more and more defiant and difficult to control.

One morning, feeling depressed and defeated, I called the local adoption agency for help. After speaking with a receptionist, who seemed to take great pleasure in telling me private adoptions rarely get access to services, she put me through to one of the nicest social workers I've ever talked to. Her name was Mary Anne, and she was exactly the person I needed at that moment.

Within minutes, my tears were flowing, and I was pouring my heart out. Without interrupting, she let me go on and on until I was about to drown in self-pity.

"She hates me," I concluded.

Then, I heard the words I was so desperate to hear: "Don't worry,

everything will be okay."

The next day I called Dr. Bennet, the therapist Mary Anne recommended. Dr. Bennet was doing research at the University of Minnesota on a disorder that seemed to affect many adopted children from Eastern Europe. She referred to it as Reactive Attachment Disorder and asked if any of the following applied to Mikala.:

Avoids eye contact	yes
Doesn't smile	yes
Doesn't want to be picked up	yes
Seems detached	yes
Ignores parent	yes
Shows little emotion	yes
Has an aversion to touching	yes
Rejects any attempt of comfort	yes
Doesn't seem to care if I exist	yes

"Anything else that seems unusual to you?"

"She won't talk to me, but she talks to herself when she thinks I'm not listening."

The Sunny Side of Crazy

A few more questions and 45 minutes later Dr. Bennet agreed that if I'd made a commitment to follow her program, we could speak by phone weekly.

Every one of our phone calls started with her reminder that patience, structure, and love were critical to success. Before she asked me how the week went, she'd remind me that it would take time for Mikala to trust and feel worthy of care.

"If you have patience and realistic expectations, everything will turn out okay."

There were days when I found that hard to believe. Not only were we struggling at home, but I'd also been called into Mikala's daycare for what was to be the first of numerous school conferences.

"This may not be the best fit for Mikala," were the first words out of the director's mouth. According to her, not only did Mikala only interact with Adam, she refused to let other children in the make-believe kitchen, And. she said, Mikala absolutely refused to lie down at naptime. In fact, she would scream until they let her get up and wander around.

I begged the director to have more patience.

"Think of all the changes she's been through, the language problem, and differences in cultures. Please ... give her a little more time."

The director agreed but insisted I explain the daycare rules to her in Japanese.

A few weeks after starting with Dr. Bennet, Mikala and I laughed together for the first time. It happened one night when

Miki finally let me lift her out of a warm bubble bath. I wrapped her in a big fluffy towel and tickled her all the way to bed.

Wonderful! Baby steps, I thought. Just like the therapist said, "it will take time. You'll know when she begins to trust you. You'll see it."

Filled with excitement, I laid her on the bed, grabbed her pj's from under the pillow, and pulled the towel away. For a split second, time stopped. The room became deafeningly quiet and very cold. I stared at Mikala's scars. Mikala stared at my face.

Mikala's eyes filled with terror as I struggled to maintain control over my emotions. But it was too late. She'd shut down, her body stiffened and an expression of resignation covered her little face. I scooped her up in my arms and rocked her back and forth until her eyelids fluttered closed.

I wanted to turn back time, erase what I'd just seen, but her terrified expression was already etched in my memory.

After I was certain she was asleep, I covered her and made my way to the kitchen to place a long-distance call to Sarah.

I asked if she was aware of Miki's secret. No, she wasn't. But she wasn't shocked either. Unlike most Japanese children who found themselves in loving families, the few that found their way to Sarah's Home were exceptions. "They often came with inaccurate or unknown histories." To confront Mikala's family would have jeopardized the adoption. What was important to Sarah was the child's welfare. That meant finding her a safe, loving home.

The Sunny Side of Crazy

" If you had known, would you have changed your mind?" she asked? She already knew the answer!

"Of course not."

The next morning I called the Japanese/American society and asked for the name of a Japanese-speaking doctor. Miracle of miracles, there was one, a pediatrician in Ann Arbor with a cancellation for the following day.

We arrived at his office twenty minutes early and spent the next two hours there.

We were greeted by one of the kindest doctors I've ever met. He took his time telling Mikala about his little sister who lived in Japan. He pulled pictures from his wallet showing a pretty high school student proudly wearing her uniform in front of a prestigious high school. He told Mikala how hard his sister had studied to be accepted there and how proud he was. "You are a smart little girl, Mikala. And, I know you are going to make your mother proud, too."

As he talked, Mikala watched his face carefully, and I watched hers. She looked curious and relaxed. She was listening carefully to every word he said.

Suddenly, her expression changed as the doctor picked her up and laid her down on a warmed exam table. He continued to talk to her as he examined her. She still looked scared but continued to watch his face as he finished the exam and gently put her down in front of a little table filled with puzzles and books.

"When did you find out?" he asked me.

I wiped away my tears and told him about all the events that had transpired since her adoption. He listened without interrupting. Then he talked to me for a long time, but all I remember was:

"Repeated abuse over a long period of time."

"No more bubble baths, watch out for infections, have her take showers, and teach her to clean herself well."

He looked over the medical form, I'd filled out and asked, "What medications is she taking?" and "How often is she having seizures?"

As much as I appreciated the kind doctor's help, my head was throbbing, and I was more than a little relieved when he finally closed Mikala's file.

"Is there anything else I need to know, Dr. Takagi? "

"There is one more thing you might need. Let me get it for you," he said as he left the room. He soon returned with a sealed envelope.

"This is documentation of my findings. You need to keep it in a safe place. It's confirmation the abuse took place before you adopted her. No abuse has happened since. Hopefully, you'll never need it."

It took me a moment to fully understand what he was saying. I never opened the envelope.

PART 2
Discovery

The Sunny Side of Crazy

CHAPTER 6
A NEW LIFE

At first, I couldn't feel anything for my new mother other than annoyance. She wanted to be close to me and I just wanted to be left alone. Not only was she always in my face, but she lied.

She lied about little things and big things all the time.

She would say "Shimpai shinai de" (don't worry) and "Dai joubu" (It will be okay) But it wasn't true then, and it still isn't. She saw nothing wrong with giving false assurances, "Don't worry Mikala, everything will be okay."

She said it when we left Miss. Sarah and Hannah at the hotel. She said it when we stepped into the airplane and again when we stepped out. She said it when we set out for my first dental appointment. "Shimpai shinai de, Dai joubu."

Mom held me in the chair while I screamed and the dentist tried to fasten a bib around my neck. I pushed him away, clamped my mouth shut, and fifteen minutes later the dentist was ready to quit. But not Mom!

"Well, I guess we'll have to spend all day and night here, Mikala."

What? Sleep here, in this chair with this thing stuck around my neck? I don't think so! I opened my mouth and let the dentist hurt me.

Going to the doctor wasn't much better. Mom held me tight while the nurses stuck needles in my arm. Then mom smiled and said, "That wasn't so bad, was it? Sometimes, her words didn't help at all.

It didn't take long to learn I could bring her to tears by resisting hugs, throwing temper tantrums, and ignoring her. But one day fate took over, and everything changed.

That morning, on my way downstairs, I tripped and tumbled down the last three steps. That was enough to break my leg in three places. I let out a blood-chilling scream, felt a searing pain, and saw a frantic mother.

I don't remember much more than that, except for a long wait to see the doctor. Mom lost her temper, and started a loud argument with the nurse. The angry nurse kept pointing toward chairs near the door and Mom, holding me tight, pushed right past her. Mom's voice brought a doctor running. I watched as the arms of his white coat flapped up and down. They reminded me of the geese flapping their wings in the pond outside. Mom held my hand tightly as a round, baby-faced doctor went through the process of putting something called a cast on my leg.

Imprisoned in a full leg cast, confined to a wheelchair, and completely helpless, I needed Mom for everything. Our world changed. I was as needy as a baby and Mom was as attentive as any new mother. We bonded in record time.

Four days after the fall, Mom pushed my wheelchair into my daycare. All eyes turned toward us and a silence fell over the room. The children stared at me while their parents and the staff's faces turned toward Mom.

The Sunny Side of Crazy

The director poked her head out of her office and moved to her door where she stood, as if her large body had become stuck in the frame.

Finally, "Oh, you can't leave her here like that. We aren't set up to accommodate handicapped children!"

Mom stared back at her for a long minute and said in a low voice "What did you say?"

"No way are we equipped or staffed to meet the demands of a handicapped child," she repeated.

"Are you refusing to accept my daughter because she's handicapped?" Mom asked in a louder voice."

"Oh, I didn't mean to give you that impression. My concern is for your daughter. She'll need special care."

Mom and the director glared at each other until the director finally broke free from the door and her silence "Why don't you come into my office?"

The parents and staff politely looked away as Mom walked into the office and the director closed the door. That is everyone, except me. I watched them through the window. I didn't need to hear words. I'd started learning to read faces the day I met Mom.

They both looked unhappy, and I wondered if I was in trouble again. *Was the director telling Mom how bad I was and how I still wouldn't lie down at nap time?*

When Mom came out of the office, she stood there looking at me for a while. Then, she gave me a great big smile. We left the center and headed for McDonald's. Mom carried me inside, set me in a booth, and said in her funny Japanese "I think it's time to celebrate Mikala, don't you?"

When we got home, Mom spent the rest of the day on the phone. By the end of the day, she explained to me what was going to happen the following day. I would go to a new daycare where all the other children would be younger. I would go to daycare in the mornings and a place called kindergarten in the afternoons. There, I would be with children my own age.

That night I complained to Sam. Sam was special. He was a secret friend. I never talked about him in Japan and wasn't planning to talk about him in America. Sam belonged to me, and I intended to keep it that way. He always made me feel better and on this night, when he said "Shimpai shinai de, dai joubu" I believed him because Sam never lied. "Don't worry, everything is going to be okay"

And, you know what? It was!

CHAPTER 7
FATE STEPPED IN

The day I started at my new daycare was beautiful. it was snowing hard and I couldn't stop looking out the window. Huge snowflakes were covering our yard in white lace. I'd never seen anything like it. There was snow in Osaka but nothing like this!

Mom came in early to get me ready. She carried me to the bathroom, put me on the toilet, helped me brush my teeth and put on my new clothes. Then, she carried me downstairs for breakfast.

As soon as I was finished eating, Mom struggled to get me into my first snowsuit. I loved its deep purple color and matching hat and gloves. It was beautiful, perfect in every way except one: one leg was missing! Mom cut it off to fit the bulky cast instead of my skinny little leg.

After getting dressed, Mom put my wheelchair in the trunk and came back to carry me to the car. She slipped and slid around to the driver's side, got in, drove to a little house down the street, got out, pulled the wheelchair out of the trunk, and carried it into the daycare. Then, she came back, carried me in, and rolled my wheelchair into the playroom.

All of the sudden, the strangest thing happened. Little children came running from every direction. They surrounded me, smiling, laughing and asking questions. As Mom struggled to take off my snowsuit, the crowd of three to five-year-old's chattered away as if they expected me to understand.

"Hi, I'm Carla,'

"I'm Joe"

"What happened to you? "

Then they turned to Mom.

"What happened to her?"

"Doesn't she talk?"

"What's her name?"

Mom leaned over and said, "Tell them your name, Honey."

"Suki" I replied.

Mom smiled again. She didn't understand. Suki in Japanese means "I like" and that was all she needed to hear.

"Miki's from a country called Japan and still has to learn a lot of English. Do you think you can help her?"

The children laughed and nodded their heads in agreement.

"And, she might also need help moving her wheelchair around. Do you think you can help with that?"

Hands went up everywhere.

"I will, I will," they all sang out.

Mom smiled and pulled two boxes of colored markers from her purse.

"And, she might forget your names. "Do you think you could write them on her cast?"

The Sunny Side of Crazy

The children looked confused and the director quickly cut in, "If you draw your pictures, I'll write your names for you." The children scrambled toward the markers as Mom slowly backed out the door.

I hardly noticed her leave. When she came back at six, the few remaining children waved and shouted, "Goodbye, Sayonara Suki." Mom was relieved. I was happy. It was a wonderful day. The next day, however, it was a whole different story.

The first day at my new daycare was so much fun I'd forgotten I had to go to a place called kindergarten the next afternoon. That morning, Mom reminded me of it just as she rolled me into the playroom.

"Don't worry, Mikala, it will be fun, everything will be--."

Before she could finish, I was surrounded by children shouting "Good morning, Suki!"

Somehow, I knew I was Suki and within minutes the children were shouting "Ohayou, Suki, Ohayou" Ohayou means good morning in Japanese and was one of the two words, I'd taught them. With my teaching going so well, I had no time to worry about what the afternoon might bring.

At noon, Rosie, a daycare helper, wheeled me into the dining room for lunch, and I remembered to worry. I worried all through lunch. I worried while she put on my snowsuit and then I worried all the way to my new school.

All I knew was that I was going to a place called kindergarten. I wanted to know more but I wasn't sure how to ask. So, I waited and worried.

The Sunny Side of Crazy

By the time Rosie rolled me into the classroom, I was shaking. She took my snowsuit off, put me in the front row, and started talking to the smiling teacher. I couldn't understand their words but I liked the teacher's face, and when the teacher came over, knelt down and said, "Hello, Mikala, I am your teacher, Ms. Smith," I liked her even more.

Suddenly, the door swung open and noisy kids in Crayola colors came running in. I knew immediately, it was not going to be anything like my nursery school back in Japan. The only thing similar was the faint smell of disinfectant.

Back in my old Japanese nursery school everyone was quiet and organized. Children stood in a long line and bowed greetings to their teachers. Here, in this new kindergarten, the children ran around like monkeys dressed in bright colors.

But by far, the biggest surprise was all their laughter. I understood right away that this school wasn't just for learning. It was also meant to be fun.

I spent the rest of the afternoon watching the class and forgetting to worry about how I'd get home. Until the bell rang!

When I heard it, I began to panic. My smiling teacher came over and helped me put my snowsuit on, pushed me outside, and walked away.

I sat there, in the snow, terrified! But, just as I felt blackness coming over me, I heard someone shouting my name. "MIKALA, MIKALA, MIKALA, where are you? Before I could say anything, there she was right in front of me. She was the strangest little lady I'd ever seen. *Who was this woman? Dressed in her dreary gray peacoat and matching woolen cap, she looked like a Japanese police captain.* She stooped down and tried to make eye contact, "Mikala?"

I was speechless! I remained silent and stared past her.

"Yes, you must be Mikala," she said as she grabbed hold of my wheelchair and pushed me to the front of the line "MOVE IT," she yelled as the children quickly cleared a path directly to the bus's door.

"COULD USE A LITTLE HELP HERE!" she shouted at the driver. I couldn't believe it, the driver jumped out of his seat, bounded down the stairs and carried me to the front seat. Then he put my wheelchair behind me and set my supplies next to me.

"She needs to be brought to the front of the line every day, understand? Got it?" The bus driver quickly nodded and responded, "Yes ma'am, yes ma'am, no problem."

"Understand?"

The bus driver nodded and quickly turned away.

Their faces, voices and pointing arms told me what was going on. I knew who was in charge. It was the woman I would come to know as Captain Cindy or simply. The Captain.

My mouth dropped open, I was in awe. I'd never seen a woman give orders to a man like that. It was surprising enough to see Mom taking care of our house without a husband, but this? *What a powerful woman she must be!*

Back at daycare, I wondered about that little lady in gray. *How did she know who I was?*

The Sunny Side of Crazy

That night, Mom told me she had a surprise. A teacher had called and offered to tutor me in English. As soon as the words were out of her mouth, I knew it had to be the strange little lady from school.

I was right! It was the captain! Mom called her Ms. Cindy, but to me, she would always be "The Captain." At my very first tutoring session, I declared war. She would talk to me, and I would give her a blank stare in return. I pretended I didn't understand a word she said. It didn't matter. The Captain had more patience and determination than any child could ever match. She put me on a three-day-a-week schedule and eventually won the war. I learned English.

When the school bell signaling the beginning of summer vacation finally rang, I was as happy as any of the other children. I'd made it through kindergarten with a total of only five seizures, no friends, and a lot more English than I'd started with.

Still, the Captain was determined I would speak perfectly by first grade, and it seemed like she was around most of that summer. Sometimes, she would pick me up at daycare and take me home before Mom arrived. That's when the Captain noticed I was a chatterbox at daycare but didn't speak at home.

Sometimes, it made her angry and she would say, "Mikala, I know you can speak. Why won't you try?"

I couldn't answer. I didn't know. I was Suki in daycare and that's how I learned English.

During that summer, something happened that I didn't understand. It didn't make sense. Mom had a special friend. His name was Uncle Mike and he brought me all kinds of presents when he came through our front door. I was beginning to look forward to his visits.

One hot day, he asked Mom if he could take me to McDonald's for ice cream.

My special friend Sam was jealous of Uncle Mike's "man of the house status" but he loved ice cream so when Mom said okay, I happily climbed into Uncle Mike's shiny new car.

I don't remember much about the trip other than being confused.

When we got home, Uncle Mike, who never yells, was shouting, "Something is wrong with Mikala. She was terrible! She kept playing with the windows, up, down, up, down. I told her to stop, and she gave me a downright evil smile. After we got the ice cream, she let it drip all over the car. She never took a bite. I know she understood me when I told her to stop and pointed to the napkins. She looked at them, then looked at me, and gave me another evil smile. She completely ignored me."

I KNOW she understood! I'm telling you, she's like Doctor Jekyll and Mr. Hyde."

I didn't understand all his words, and it was many years before I knew who Dr. Jekyll and Mr. Hyde were, but it didn't matter. Uncle Mike was angry and Mom was even angrier. He shouted and Mom shouted louder. The door slammed, and he was gone for a long time. At least, it seemed like a long time. Eventually, Uncle Mike came back, but it was a lot longer before he brought me any more presents.

51

The Sunny Side of Crazy

CHAPTER 8
COMPANIONS AND CLASSES

Even though I knew more English by the end of summer, I still wasn't ready for first grade. I'd learned early on to match my mom's and teacher's expressions, but I didn't really understand what they were saying.

The Captain practically lived at our home that summer and Mom stopped speaking Japanese altogether. It seemed like they had teamed up to get me through first grade.

The Captain never became angry at me, even when I pretended I'd forgotten everything. Twenty minutes into each session, we would both be exhausted. I'd put my head down on the table and pretend I'd fallen asleep. Still, she wouldn't stop. She'd just open a book and begin to read. Before she'd finish, I really would be sound asleep. Often, I didn't even hear her leave.

The Captain suggested Mom put me in a special education class, but Mom wouldn't hear of it. At the time, Mom thought any and all problems could be solved with enough love, time and attention

As it turned out, the Captain may have been right. I struggled and school made me more anxious than ever. My seizures increased, and the teachers were terrified. When I'd seize, the teacher would call the Captain out of her special ed. class, and when I'd come to, the Captain would be sitting on the floor stroking my head and telling me everything was going to be okay.

After each seizure, Mom would take me back to her doctor. The doctor would increase my medication, and before long, I was falling asleep in class. I'd wake up to my classmates exchanging glances and giggling at me. And CJ, the class bully, would put his head down and pretend to snore. Everyone seemed to think that was really funny.

I didn't tell Mom because I'd already learned that if I told her anything she didn't want to hear, she'd turn up at school the very next morning. It happened my first week of first grade.

"Mom, Why can't I stand up with my class?"

"You can," she answered.

"No, I can't," I insisted.

"Of course, you can," she replied.

"No, I shook my head, no I can't,"

"Miki, you don't use crutches anymore. Your leg is fine. Of course, you can stand up."

"No, I can't!"

"Why can't you stand up?"

"The teacher won't let me.

"Miki, I'm sure the teacher knows you can stand up."

"She won't let me stand up."

"I'm pretty sure she will, Miki"

The Sunny Side of Crazy

"Okay, Mom."

The next day when I walked into my classroom, Mom was already there. From that day on I stood up with the rest of the class when they said the Pledge of Allegiance. Mom said the teacher thought I was a foreigner.

By the end of first grade, the only friends I had were my secret friends Sam and Suki, and the little children at daycare. I spent most of my time alone with Sam. If it hadn't been for him, it would have been a terrible year. Sam was lonely, too. So, when he begged me to let him talk to Mom, I gave in. Before my accident, Sam worried that our new mom might send us back, or worse yet, give us to another foreign mother. Every night Sam would beg me to try to get along with her, but I didn't worry about it. Who would want a little girl that was so bad her family gave her away anyway?

By first grade, Sam and I believed Mom would probably be our forever mother, and it was time to introduce him.

It didn't go well. We'd just finished putting a Disney puzzle together and walked into the kitchen where Mom was cooking dinner.

"Hi, I'm Sam," Sam said.

Mom looked at me with a bewildered smile and said "Is Sam your imaginary friend, Miki ?"

What? I wasn't sure what she meant. Were my secret friends called imaginary friends?

Mom continued to look confused. "Is Sam your imaginary friend?" she repeated.

I stood there staring at her. *Was she blind? Didn't she see Sam? Is that what imaginary means?*

"Would you like to have dinner with us, Sam?" Mom asked.

Sam nodded, "Okay, I guess so."

"Well, dinner's almost ready. Why don't you put your puzzle away and go wash your hands?" Mom turned back to the stove and continued cooking as if Sam hadn't been there at all.

I was devastated! So was Sam.

If Mom didn't see Sam, maybe no one did. And I'd have to keep him a secret forever.

Sam never asked to meet Mom again.

I thought about a story Mom read at bedtime. It was about beautiful guardian angels. She told me it was a true story and even though you couldn't see them, every child had them. So, for a while, I thought maybe Sam was an angel. After all, he protected me and helped me do things I couldn't do for myself.

Summer vacation brought a couple of big surprises. The first was our trip to Walt Disney World and the second was the appearance of Calle. Mom had promised to take me to Disney World before I started first grade, but my broken leg put an end to that plan.

By the time my cast was taken off, I had a new doctor, one that gave us very bad news. My leg hadn't been set correctly, and Mom had to make a decision: have my leg re-broken and reset, or accept the fact that I may walk with a slight limp. Resetting would mean breaking my leg in the three places it had been broken before and making adjustments. I remember mom crying that night.

We made it to Disney World right after I finished first grade, and it was beyond anything I could have imagined. I loved it! Fantasy land, Epcot Center, and even the International Market. In fact, I think that was the first time Calle made an appearance.

On the last day at the park, we had lunch at Cinderella's castle and then went to the Japanese Pavilion for last-minute gifts. The Japanese market was filled with pretty things from Japan. It only took Mom a minute to notice the children's colorful kimonos hanging inside the entrance. She picked out three of the brightest, and we headed into the dressing room.

I put on the brightest one and when I looked in the mirror, I saw a reflection smiling back. I couldn't believe it was me. Whoever she was, she was beautiful.

Mom said that was the right kimono, and I begged her to let me wear it back to the hotel. Reluctantly she agreed, but said she didn't want to hear me complain about people staring at me.

She needn't have worried. As soon as we walked out of the market, I turned into someone else. Suddenly, I became a star surrounded by Disney visitors pointing and clicking their cameras at me. Before, I'd hated people looking at me, especially with their cameras in hand. But, that day, I found myself happily posing for tourists just as if I were part of the cast. Mom laughed and said this was a side of me she'd never seen before. That side had a name, Calle.

The Sunny Side of Crazy

Back home, Calle wasn't around much. I wanted to be alone. I was finding second grade difficult. Schoolwork was hard, and the harder it became, the more seizures I had. After each seizure, Mom would take me back to the doctor who would increase my medication yet again. Then, I'd sleep through most of my classes.

That came to a sudden end the night an exhausted Mom returned from a business trip in Houston.

She'd left me in the Captain's care, and I was angry, so angry, I refused to open Mom's "I didn't forget you" gift.

We were both out of sorts and barely said a word to each other during dinner. Mom silently cleared the table and started to wash the dishes. With a pout on my face, I stood next to her staring at her. She paid no attention to me, and I flew into a rage. Determined to distract her, I slowly reached for the shiny butcher knife sitting on the counter. I knew better, and she reminded me again, "Mikala no, you don't touch knives, remember? Don't touch that! Mikala, NO! I said NO!"

My fingers had just curled around the knife handle when I heard Mom's voice louder than ever. "Stop Miki, I said don't touch!"

Just as my lips began to tremble a pan of very warm, soapy water hit my face. Water dripped from the top of my head to the tips of my toes. I was soaked and shocked.

For a moment, time stopped. Mom and I stood there staring at each other. I closed my eyes, took a breath and screamed, but I never had another seizure. The doctor discontinued my medication and told Mom not to ever do it again.

The Sunny Side of Crazy

Both Mom and the Captain doubled their efforts to get me through second grade. We went through workbooks weeks before the rest of my class. Still, despite their help, my report cards reflected varied performance, and I received the same comments year after year.

Produces inconsistent work

Is easily distracted

Needs to learn to focus

Struggles to manage her time

Does not take responsibility for missing or late work

Early one morning, just before the end of the school year, the principal told our class, in a serious flat voice that our teacher had died. We would have a substitute for the rest of the year. Not sure how to react, I looked around the room. To my surprise, all my classmates looked sad. A few were even crying. That night, I told Mom my teacher was dead and asked her what that meant.

"Everyone dies, Miki, but usually not until they are old. I don't think your teacher was old, but I guess God needed her in heaven."

"What's heaven?"

"A beautiful place that you only go after you die. We can't see it now, but that's where God and the angels live."

"Are you sure?"

Mom gave me a funny look. "Yes, Honey, I'm sure."

The Sunny Side of Crazy

I wondered why she said heaven and angels were real but thought my friend Sam and probably my other imaginary friends weren't. Mom looked too sad to ask, and I didn't feel like crying, so I just said good night and went to bed. The next day I wore a sad face just like the other children.

By the time second grade ended, Uncle Mike was back, and Sam became his little helper. I thought Uncle Mike would want a little boy to help him so I'd asked Sam to help. Every weekend, I'd get up early, put on shorts and a t-shirt and wait for Uncle Mike to arrive. Then, we'd start working on Mom's dream deck. Mom had visions of a beautiful cedar deck built around what was left of a broken-down, in-ground pool next to our house. While Uncle Mike and Sam worked on the deck, Mom glued padding to the sides of the pool in preparation for the beautiful blue liner that would soon be installed over it. It looked like everything would be finished in time to celebrate Labor Day.

Unfortunately, it didn't work out that way. In her enthusiasm, Mom forgot to take into account the wildlife waiting for the pool's opening.

Within days of completion, a family of beavers moved in and chewed holes in the liner. Mom quickly patched the holes and bravely held to her plan for a Labor day celebration. Soon a couple of families of ducks moved in with dozens of fuzzy little babies.

Uncle Mike and I were ready to give up. But, not Mom! Every morning she grabbed her net, chased ducks, and relocated families back to the river. By the end of the summer, besides the ducks, she'd saved one angry black cat, two dogs, and one tired opposum. Still, she wouldn't give up. And, that year it stormed all Labor Day weekend too!

The third grade could have been better but, then it could have been a whole lot worse, too. C.J, the class bully had become mean enough to bring any kid to tears. Thanks to Calle, it wasn't always me!

In first grade, he'd laugh as I seized and fell asleep. In second grade, he enjoyed throwing spitballs at me. For two years his teasing and imitations had made me miserable. I was so tired of hearing his stupid, "Open your eyes zzz's and learn eeeezzz to speakeeee English."

But, he was in for a surprise on the first day of the third grade.

"Hey, Miki, lookeee at me!" he taunted, as he pretended to shake and roll his eyes.

At first, I didn't recognize him. The skinny little second grader was fat. I mean he must have spent all summer eating HoHos.

"C.J, Is that you? Calle shot back. What happened? you don't look like you!" I paused.

Did I say that?

His expression told me all I needed to know. He was embarrassed by his belly hanging over his belt, He knew his face was larger and his eyes smaller. And, he probably knew his nose had turned into more of a snout. To add to that, his baby soft skin was showing early signs of zits.

He was more than a little angry. I could see the fury in his eyes and would have been scared, but Calle didn't seem to care. C.J. became her target for the rest of the year. Before long, my special friend Calle had become the third grades entertainment. She was the class clown. Laughing at herself was easy. And, as hard as C.J. would try, Calle always managed to get the last laugh.

Ms. Casey, my teacher was frustrated and called Mom weekly complaining about my disruptions. She begged her to talk to me.

Mom was confused by what she didn't see at home. One night, Mom asked,

"Mikala. Why did you write 'C.J. farts' on the board?

"I don't remember doing that."

"Ms. Casey said you did, and you were very disruptive in class again."

"Well Mom, he does fart. Ms. Casey should put him in the back of the room so the rest of us don't have to smell him. But, anyway, Mom, I didn't do it. Someone else must-have."

Eventually, Ms. Casey decided to take matters into her own hands. She sent me out into the hall time-out cubicle; It was Calle's favorite place. There, we could spend our time daydreaming and sleeping, Things were looking up.

Even better, toward the end of the school year, the caseworker who'd done Mom's home study called with a request.

The Sunny Side of Crazy

His agency was planning an international fashion show to introduce their new China program. They wanted a little Asian girl to star in the show. Would it be possible for me to model?

The following day, when Mom told me about the call, she said she'd told them no because I was much too shy. Calle exploded. Why Mom? Why would you say that?

"Because you don't like people looking at you."

" Mom, Yes, I do! I can do it. I did it at Disney. I want to. Mom, please? Call him back!"

Mom tried to talk me out of it but she was talking to Calle, and Calle wouldn't stop. Mom reluctantly called and told them I'd be there.

I spent my summer vacation both worrying about and looking forward to the coming show. Sometimes, I could see myself in front of an applauding audience, other times, I'd see myself tripping over my kimono and landing flat on my face.

Fear and fame, fear and fame, the audience laughing, the audience clapping. Mom saw my changing moods and said she'd better call and tell them I'd changed my mind.

Still, Calle wouldn't hear of it, so Mom focused on trying to convince me that the world wouldn't end if I couldn't go through with it at the last moment. For me, that was encouraging.

I needn't have worried. Calle arrived and appeared all sunshine and giggly the morning of the show. She babbled on and on as Mom clipped flowers into my silky, long hair. Then, she helped put on my kimono.

"No, Miki, you have to place the left side over the right. Remember Miki, only the dead can have the right placed over the left."

Calle burst out laughing, fell back and lay motionless on the bed. Mom broke out laughing, too. Once again, she said this was a side of me she didn't often see. I didn't either. But when I looked in the mirror, I liked what I saw.

On the way to the agency, Calle rambled on and on about how pretty she looked and how much she loved the kimono. It was the one Mom bought me at the airport years before. Calle thanked Mom for buying it and I wondered how Calle knew about the airport.

Finally, it was performance time! All the seats were filled, the Japanese music began, and to those soft notes, Calle made her way on to the stage. She strutted between paper cherry trees, paused, looked directly at the audience, and then made her way to the end of the makeshift runway.

There, she stopped again and bowed to the audience. She smiled as cameras clicked and holding her parasol high, she turned and walked back to the center of the stage. Once again, she turned, smiled and bowed low before leaving the stage. Whistles, applause and clicking cameras, followed her and she loved every moment of it.

After the show, the audience surrounded her asking questions and taking more pictures. Couple after couple signed up for the coming orientation. They all wanted a little Asian daughter of their own.

The Sunny Side of Crazy

The agency was thrilled, Mom was impressed, and I was happy. Thanks to my friend, Calle, there are probably more than a few lucky Chinese girls living with forever families. I just didn't expect one of them to be my little sister.

The next day, when Mom told me she'd filled out an application to adopt another little girl, I was devastated. "No, thanks, I don't want a little sister." I'd been replaced by one before. Why would I want one now? I didn't speak to Mom for days.

Fourth grade had barely started when Mom came into my bedroom waving an envelope from China. Inside was a picture of my new little sister.

"Miki, look we got a picture of your new little sister."

Acting like I couldn't care less, I took the envelope from her hand, pulled out the picture, and burst out laughing. She was the funniest looking little girl I'd ever seen. A little round face topped off by a silly pigtail that stood straight up on the top of her head. I told Mom she looked like Mr. Potato Head or a scared rabbit.

"Her name is Fu Ying. Oh Miki, isn't she cute?"

I didn't think so, but I liked her name. Right then and there, I nicknamed her "Little Bunny FuFu", a nickname that remains to this day. It was close to the end of the year when Mom finally got a clearance date to go to China. By then, I'd almost forgotten all about it.

For most of the fourth grade, I was completely occupied with two obsessions, Full House with the Olsen twins' show on TV and my teacher Ms. Dixon. The Olsen twins looked alike but were very different. Oddly, I felt I was the same. I told Mom over and over, I thought I had twins but, of course, she told me I didn't have a twin, let alone more than one.

I talked constantly about Mary Kate and Ashley and begged Mom to buy me every product they sold. That came to an end the day I threw a tantrum because she wouldn't take me on one of their summer cruises. Their cruises were limited to only eight hundred passionate fans, who, if they were lucky, would see and maybe even talk to the famous twins. That's the only time I remember Mom saying I was crazy

"Mikala, you're crazy. I promise you a cruise is NOT going to happen!"

The obsession with my fourth-grade teacher was a bigger problem. I thought Ms. Dixon was perfect. I wanted to be just like her.

I dressed in a plaid skirt with a tailored white shirt just like she did. I wore headbands that matched hers and arrived in class early every morning. I was also always the last one to leave. I even memorized her schedule so I could run into her in the hall. Then, she betrayed me.

Three months after school started, Mom was called into the principal's office for a meeting with Ms. Dixon and the principal. Ms. Dixon proceeded to tell my surprised mom that she was scared of me. She told Mom, not only did I dress like her and hang around before and after class, I was stalking her in the halls.

That night Mom told me about the meeting. She didn't ask me why I was doing it. She simply said. "Mikala, you need to stay away from your teacher. Do not go into the classroom early, stay late or try to run into her in the halls. Just stay away from her."

I was in shock. *How could the teacher I idolized so much betray me? I was so loyal. How could she be so mean?* I've never forgiven her.

That year, summer couldn't come fast enough. When it finally did., Mom was ready to leave for China. I had adjusted to the idea that I would soon be the big sister to a two-year-old and was almost excited about it. I thought I was going to China, too but as Mom so often does, she changed her mind and decided to go alone. That way, she said, I would have time to play with little Bunny Fu Fu before returning to school. By the time summer was over, I was anxious to get back to school.

Not that I didn't like controlling Fu. I did. And because she adored me, she let me. I doubt there are many pictures that don't show us hugging, or me pushing her around. Mom would say,

"Stop controlling her Miki," or "Miki take your hands off Fu." But Fu didn't mind, so why should I? I'd say "Okay Mom. Wait a couple of minutes and say, "Hey, Fu wanna play choo choo?" and off we'd go again.

I fell in love with her but at the same time, I was jealous. After all, before she came I was the center of attention. After she came everything changed. Mom gave her a beautiful name, Kimberly Jade, and she was as charming and cute, as she was embarrassing.

I hated going anywhere with her. She loved men, all men. And, they seemed to think she was the cutest little thing under the sun. When we were in the car, she would sit in her little car seat, smile and wave at every man that passed.

As if that weren't bad enough, she learned English quickly and by the end of summer, she would sit in the grocery cart and focus on any man unlucky enough to be shopping alone. Then, in her sweet little voice, she would say, "Excuse me, Mister, will you marry my mother?" I wanted to die, but Mom just laughed it off.

"I'd like to Honey, but I already have a wife at home."

"Maybe, you'd better ask your mother first, Sweetie "

Or "hmm, let me think about it."

Back at home, Mom would say, "Miki, maybe Fu had a father who loved her, one that she misses. *That made no sense. If she did, why would they give her away? The thought that Fu might have had a father that loved her bothered me.*

One day, shortly after that, I followed Fu down the hall for breakfast and just as we reached the top of the stairs, my arms shot out in front of me pushing her down the stairs. Fu made a complete airborne summersault before landing in Mom's outstretched arms. I stood there in shock. I didn't remember following or pushing her, but my arms were straight out in front of me. Mom said I pushed her and had an ugly smirk on my face that she had never seen before. I think that was the first time Tin appeared but it wasn't the last.

It was a long time before Mom trusted me to be alone with Fu again. But one day, several weeks later, she asked me to watch Fu while she went to the store. She said she wasn't going to be gone long, but it was just long enough for us to get into trouble.

"Want to play beauty shop FuFu? "

I didn't wait for an answer. She always wanted to play. I went into Mom's room and came back with scissors. "Now, don't move, sit still while I make you pretty."

She sat expectantly while I went to work. Snip, snip here, snip, snip there. Not quite short enough, I cut closer and closer to her scalp. Patches of baldness began to appear and I kept on clipping. When there was nothing left to cut, I held up the mirror. Fu took one look and burst out laughing. I laughed right along with her until Mom walked in the door.

"Oh my God, Miki, what have you done?"

"Nothing, we were just playing ------"

"Miki Get in the car, right now, Did you hear me? Right now!"

Mom picked up Fu and headed for the car! Without looking at either of us, she buckled Fu in and drove to the nearest Cheap Cuts. Mom pushed us in the door and said, "Shave their heads!"

I panicked. What? She must be kidding. I couldn't go back to school with no hair!"

"Mom, no please, no. We were just playing."

Mom ignored me.

"Shave their heads!" she repeated to the smiling beautician.

The Sunny Side of Crazy

"I'll do the best I can," the beautician responded as she placed a plastic cape around little Fu's neck.

Fu watched as the rest of her hair fell to the floor. She looked at Mom and smiled. She looked exactly like a little Buddhist monk.

"Your turn," Mom said as Fu climbed out of the chair.

The beautician ran her hands through my long silky hair.

"She has beautiful hair, are you sure you want me to cut it off? "

This time Mom didn't say shave, she simply replied," Cut it off."

I returned to school with a very short french cut that Calle and Suki loved. I was just happy to have any hair at all.

By fifth grade, I was falling behind and had given up all hope of catching up. I asked Suki, who loved learning, to help me but even with Suki's help, I was failing. It was clear she could memorize anything, but fifth-grade classes required more than just memorization. I was expected to think. I wasn't good at figuring things out and had little idea what was expected of me.

Most of the fifth-grade girls were already talking about boobs and boys, and most boys were talking about boobs and girls. Bodies were changing and curiosity was running wild.

I was uncomfortable with my body and the flirty atmosphere I found myself in For me, it was a year of teasing and being the target of jokes.

Mom understood this and was reluctant to sign my permission slip for the optional fifth-grade sex education class. I didn't want to be the only student sitting out, so she finally signed. The evening after the class she asked her usual dinner time question,

"So, how was school today Miki?"

I stared at her. Surely she didn't want me to talk about my disgusting class in front of Fufu.

"Miki, are you okay? How was school?"

"Which part? Any? All?"

"Miki," she repeated, "Did you have a good day?"

"Not really, I didn't like the special class you signed me up for"

I could tell by the look on her face she'd forgotten all about the class.

"Well, we can talk about it after dinner, okay?"

"No, we don't have to."

After Mom had put Fu to bed, she asked me again. "How was school today, Miki?"

I hesitated and tried to hold back what was bothering me but, I couldn't.

"Mom," I blurted out," Why did Ms. Brown say we need to practice?"

"Practice what?"

"Sex." She said we need to practice sex."

"She said, what?"

"She said we should always remember to practice safe sex. She wants us to practice safe sex."

"Mikala, you are not to practice sex, any kind of sex. Do you hear me?"

The expression on Mom's face was new. It was almost worth the lecture about consequences and the silly hour she spent trying to explain other confusing English expressions like when the cows come home, or you can't un-ring the bell. Her explanations didn't make any sense and just further confused me. Mom was convinced I still wasn't sure how, when, and where the term "practice safe sex" was meant to apply, so she was in my class before I arrived the following day. That afternoon Ms. Brown told the whole class she may have misspoken and tried to clarify what my classmates already knew.

By the end of the year, my classmates were looking forward to junior high. I was dreading it. I begged Mom to send me to St. Mary's, the local Catholic school known for its separation of sexes, strict teachers and firm discipline.

"Mikala, I wish I could, but it's a luxury I can't afford."

I was disappointed. There would be no escaping stuck-up girls or fat C.J. and his stupid jokes.

Not long after that, on a beautiful afternoon, Fu was taking a nap and Mom had her nose stuck in a book while I sat on the stairs alone, bored and restless. I reached into my pocket and felt for a paper clip. I knew exactly what I was going to do with it.

I pulled it out, straightened it slowly, and jammed it into the smooth skin on the inside of my arm. I was fascinated. Drops of blood began to bubble up. I pushed it in deeper and deeper until dark red blood began to flow. Still fascinated, I began dragging the clip across my arm, until I heard Mom scream.

"What the hell are you doing, Miki? What are you thinking? Give me that! Give it to me now! You will never do that again! Do you hear me? NEVER, NEVER, NEVER! Do you hear me, Mikala? Do you?"

I nodded and handed Mom the paper clip.

" Have you done this before, Miki?"

I stared at her confused. I didn't know.

She pulled me into the bathroom and cleaned my arm.

"Why Miki, Why would you do that?"

I didn't answer her. Truthfully, I didn't know. It just felt like the right thing to do at the time. I was so focused, intent on what I was doing. I didn't remember any reason or any pain.

I never cut again but I went to therapy and to St. Mary's Junior High.

The Sunny Side of Crazy

CHAPTER 9
THROUGH A MOTHER'S EYES

Mikala made it through elementary school, and I should have gotten an award for attending more teacher's meetings than any other parent.

Some were about her performance but most were about behavior. I'm at a loss to understand what is going on. It's a behavior I have never seen at home. I know her teachers were being truthful, but Mikala insists she didn't do the things they've told me she's done.

At one of the very first teacher's meetings, her teacher told me she'd climbed up on top of her desk and started swinging her sweater around in circles.

Even her teacher was shocked. She said it seemed so out of character, she wouldn't have believed it if she hadn't seen it with her own eyes.

"Mikala is a well-behaved student ninety-nine percent of the time, but once in a while, she does something absolutely bizarre."

When I ask Mikala why, she just stares at me and says, "I don't know."

If I ask her about a teacher's specific comment, she says, The teacher's wrong, she didn't do it or she doesn't remember.

Over the years, Miki and I have attended numerous therapy sessions. None of the therapists could explain her unusual behavior. Dr. Owens said she had a learning disability. Dr. Evant talked about disorders but suggested we focus on specific behaviors and what triggers them. Months later, Mikala's behavior always remained just as unpredictable as ever and the triggers unknown.

Throughout primary school, I made excuses. By the time she was ready for junior high school, I could no longer stay in denial. Something was seriously wrong. Eating problems, lying, and cutting were all signs she needed serious help. I found a therapist who was well known for working with preteens. She realized the seriousness of Mikala's problems and immediately scheduled Miki for twice-a-week sessions.

With the therapist's encouragement, I enrolled Mikala at Saint Mary's Catholic School and made plans to send her to a Catholic summer camp for a week before starting school. She helped me find the perfect camp. One with a great reputation and the pictures were awesome. Located in Northern Wisconsin, it offered all kinds of sports, safety precautions and an abundance of counselors.

Along with the normal application and health information they required, the camp had an unusual request. They wanted a "snowball" letter for each child to open the last evening at camp. The snowball letter was to include everything we admired and loved about our child.

I didn't expect that! When I sat down to write Mikala's letter, I realized how much I'd focused on our problems and how little time I'd spent thinking about the positive days. There had been many. I could have listed our problems in fifteen minutes.

The Sunny Side of Crazy

It took me over an hour to finish my letter but I enjoyed every minute of it.

I suppose the objective was for the campers to receive "Atta boys" from their parents. In my case, it was a wake-up call. Mikala and I had just gone through a difficult year, but too often, I'd let clouds overshadow our sunny days. By the time I finished writing the snowball letter, I was smiling.

The Sunny Side of Crazy

CHAPTER 10
MOSQUITO PREP

I suppose Mom thought sending me to a religious summer camp would prepare me for St. Mary's. She was raised Catholic but converted to something indescribable during her years in Japan, While there, she took part in Shinto and Buddhist ceremonies, attended mass, and visited her missionary friend's tent meetings. Back in America, she attended several different churches, but for the sake of my education, she became Catholic again.

She was right, I got a taste of Catholicism but the mosquitoes got more than a taste of me. The camp may have been as beautiful as heaven but, for me, it was pure hell. It was hot, sticky, and full of nature's critters and smells, especially around the outhouses.

The camp was located on the banks of a forgotten lake in Wisconsin and inhabited by millions of mosquitoes that I'm sure were looking forward to summer camp more than the campers.

We lived by a strict schedule. We were up at 6:30 for prayers and a short lecture before lining up with 60 other campers for an all-you-can-eat breakfast of corn flakes, oatmeal, runny eggs, cold toast and yogurt. If you were lucky and, among the first in line, you got a carton of orange juice and a carton of milk. Midway through, you could choose one or the other.

The Sunny Side of Crazy

After breakfast, campers returned to their assigned cabins and changed to swimsuits for beach time. I was lucky because I wore a size eight and could swim, so I was put in the shark's group. The girls who couldn't keep their heads above water were called minnows and the remaining group, made-up of girls size eighteen and above and those who could only float were called dolphins. The mean girls called them whales.

Before lunch, we returned to our cabins where we could read from an assortment of books about saints and miracles, or take a nap. I spent my time daydreaming about my comfortable bed at home and wondering what my classmates were doing while I was stuck in this forsaken camp. Lunch followed at exactly noon, and after that more time to read, bond with other campers, or pour our hearts out to a camp counselor.

At three-thirty sharp, there were team sports. We were given a choice between volleyball or soccer. I chose volleyball thinking the other girls would be less likely to notice my slight limp.

Before dinner, more prayers. After dinner, a short lecture on living like saints followed by the best part of our day, fireside chats served with an abundance of s'mores. It was meant to be a sacred time where we could share our hopes and fears. But in truth, most of the girls were more interested in gossiping and eating sweets.

That's when I realized I wasn't completely different from the other girls. Everyone was worried about fitting in. Some of the campers told Father Benjamin it wasn't possible to fit in and still live a saintly life. He argued that it was. One of the campers asked how he would know since she'd heard priests didn't want to have sex. He said that wasn't entirely true and quickly changed the subject. Some of the girls giggled, others laughed, but at the time, I had no idea what they were talking about so I just sat there quietly waiting for the s'mores.

On the last night of camp everyone was in a great mood, happy to be returning to their mosquito-free homes. Some of the girls hugged and promised to keep in touch. A few cried, probably relieved they'd survived and were finally able to leave.

On that night, Father Benjamin shouted, "Gather around the fire everyone. Sit down, I have a surprise." It turned out the camp had an address after all, and our parents knew it. They were required to write us a "snowball" letter in which they wrote only positive things and reminded us of how much we were loved.

After a quick prayer, Father Benjamin began calling out names. One by one, we walked up, took our letter, and returned to our cabins. Most of us anyway. One of my cabin mates didn't get a letter. She came back to the cabin long after the rest of us had gone to bed. It was dark, but in the moonlight, I could see her eyes were swollen. A camp counselor sat on her bunk with her. They didn't talk. They just sat together. When I woke up. I looked for her but she wasn't there. She wasn't at breakfast either.

I didn't think much about how happy the other girls were to be leaving camp, but I thought a lot about her. I wondered if she was happy to be going home. I think it was the first time I really felt sorry for someone else. I was glad the one girl who didn't get a letter wasn't me.

The Sunny Side of Crazy

CHAPTER 11
JUNIOR HIGH HIGHS

After two weeks of camp, I was worried about what Catholic school would be like. I shouldn't have. St. Mary's was a hundred times better than I expected. It was a girls' school where all the students looked pretty much the same in their blue plaid skirts, white shirts and navy blue sweaters. I was the only one who was different. I tried to blend in by tying my sweater around my waist as they did and copying their hairstyles but I couldn't hide my differences.

Our teacher, Sister Mary Agnes wore a habit identical to the other nuns at Saint Marys. It was an ugly long shift that probably came in two sizes, skinny and fat. Sister Mary Agnes would have worn skinny. Beneath the shift, she wore wicked witch boots that clicked when she walked. Her only accessory was a simple silver cross hanging on a chain around her skinny waist. On her head was something that looked like a bucket trimmed in lace. Whatever it was, it covered all but a few strands of her frizzy gray hair.

On the first day of class, Sister Mary Agnes stood in front of the room with an expressionless face and informed us that she was a stickler for rules. "If you follow them, do your homework and turn it in on time, we should get along just fine."

She picked up a list of names from her desk.

"When I call your name, say here and hold your hand up high so I can see you!"

One by one, she called our names, and one by one each student raised their hand and said "here." Sister Mary Agnes paused, looked at each one for an intense minute, and then moved on. She'd almost come to my name when she called out,

"Josephine Landers?"

There was no reply.

"Josephine Landers?" she repeated.

"Oh, do you mean Joey Landers? Yep, that would be me," came a loud voice from the back of the room.

"OH, DO YOU MEAN, HERE, SISTER MARY AGNES? THAT WOULD BE ME." Sister Mary Agnes replied in a tone we would come to know well.

I turned and glanced at the voice from the back of the room and saw a stunning girl with sun-streaked hair staring directly back at Sister Mary Agnes.

"Okay, got it," she replied while flashing the sister a charming, yet challenging, smile.

I didn't know what to make of her. I'd been watching faces for a long time, and I knew she'd just declared war.

I was lost in thought when I heard my name called. I quickly looked up, raised my hand, and in a shaky voice said, "I'm here."

"Louder," shouted Sister Mary Agnes.

I raised my hand higher and in a still-shaky but louder voice said, "I'm here Sister Mary Agnes."

All the while I could feel Joey grinning. I looked back at her and she smiled at me.

As we left class, I heard her voice behind me.

"So, how old do you think she is?"

"What?"

"How old do you think the sister is?" Joey repeated.

"Hard to tell," I responded.

"Older than she looks," Joey whispered as she headed to her locker.

I looked back at Sister Mary Agnes. It was impossible to tell.

That night I wrote about Joey, my new classmate, in my journal. My secret friends wrote back. Suki loved Joey's intelligence. Calle loved her boldness, humor and competitiveness and Sam thought she was nice. Tin didn't write anything at all. Sam and I liked Joey because she liked me.

Early on, my journals had become the primary means of communication between my secret friends and myself. Shortly after starting sixth grade, a new entry appeared. It simply said I like Joey, too, Skye. Skye was soon to become another of my secret friends.

Sixth grade was a wonderful year. I made a best friend, one named Joey. And, I'd discovered another secret friend named Skye. Skye seemed to know everything about everyone, but I didn't know a thing about her.

The Sunny Side of Crazy

Our whole family was happy that year. My friendship with Joey gave my little sister time away from our choo choo train games. She spent hours with Mom, and I wasn't jealous. I had a busy life. My secret friends came more often. Sometimes I knew they were coming, other times I only knew they'd come by the mess they left behind.

One of the perks of my friendship with Joey was the Beanie connection. During junior high, Beanie Babies were all the rage. Joey talked little about her father and when she did, it was in a most unflattering way. She was convinced he had another family in China and would never come back for more than a few weeks at a time. He was an absentee father who worked and lived abroad. But every time he came back he showed his love by bringing us the newest Beanies.

Because I was her best friend, when he was in town he would take us out for pizza and give us the newest editions. He would write down the names of which Beanies we still wanted and bring them back on his next visit.

Joey always laughed when I'd remind her to thank him, I'd say, "It's so nice of him" And Joey would reply. "Well, You know my dad, Miki, he likes Asian girls!"

That whole year was full of sunshine and by the time the school year ended, Joey and I were best friends. We spent a lot of the summer vacation just goofing around and getting to know each other better. The more I learned, the more impressed I was. Not only was Joey in an advanced gymnastics class but she was also a potential Olympic candidate. And, as far as school work, she hardly had to open a book. She remembered everything! She was brilliant, beautiful and bold. I often wondered why she enjoyed hanging out with me.

The weekend before seventh grade, Joey and I spent a whole day at the mall. It was one of those perfect days. Just before five, happy and exhausted, we headed for the diner where our mothers planned to meet us.

I couldn't wait to show Mom and Fu all my purchases. As soon as I got home I threw my bags on my bed and stripped down to my underwear. Fu and Mom waited in the front room for my post-shopping fashion show.

I tore open the first bag and stepped back in shock. Those clothes weren't mine! *Wait a minute, did I bring home Joey's bags?* I sat down on my bed and looked at the purchases. *No, I couldn't have bought those things. We didn't even go into those shops. Joey certainly wouldn't have bought anything from Victoria Secret. She hated that place! And, the rest of the things. Well, they certainly weren't Joey's taste in clothes.*

I sat on my bed and stared at the purchases, skinny jeans, a short spandex skirt, and an imitation black leather jacket. *"Where were the plaid flannel shirts and big baggy jeans I'd bought?"*

I peeked in the pretty pink bag. No cotton briefs, just a couple of pairs of bikinis, a thong, and two padded lace bras.

Confused, I sat on my bed staring at the purchases and trying to make sense of what had happened. I picked up the phone and dialed Joey's number.

"Joey, do I have your bags ?"

"What, Of course not. Why?"

I don't remember buying all this stuff.?

Joey laughed. "Miki, You can't say I didn't warn you. Your mom threw a fit, didn't she?"

"Not yet," I replied as I hung up the phone.

I hid the bags in the back of my closet, told Mom I had a headache and would model some other time. Confused, and concerned, I climbed into bed wondering how I'd return my new wardrobe. It took a couple of weeks but I did it.

Seventh Grade was even better than sixth. Everything was perfect. Thanks to my secret friend Skye who helped me develop volleyball skills and Calle who helped me make the class laugh, I was accepted! I mean both Joey and I were on the fringe, but we weren't left out. Everyone knew we were different but they didn't seem to care.

My secret friends were around when I needed them, and I didn't worry about blackouts, weird behavior, or being left out anymore.

Once in a while, I would catch Joey watching me with an inquisitive, crooked smile and I'd wonder what I'd done, but she never said anything, so I'd let it pass.

At home, things were going well, too. Little bunny Fu Fu was growing up and out of her nickname. She wanted me to call her by her formal name, Kimberly Jade. But, because I was jealous of the name Mom had given her and I loved her nick name, I began to call her Fu.

The Sunny Side of Crazy

Sister Mary Agnes wasn't having much fun that year. Joey enjoyed messing with her, and I enjoyed watching. We'd noticed Sister was a very picky eater. We'd watch her pick at her little lunch, set her fork down, wipe her mouth and read. If there was anything sweet or sticky on her plate, she would look at it disapprovingly and move it to the side of the plate. Two minutes before class, she would dump leftover food and all sweets in the garbage.

Midway through the year, Joey decided to leave something sticky and sweet on her desk before each morning's class. Joey's mother was happy to purchase a goody for the good Sister when she stopped for coffee in the morning. Joey would place the treat on a paper towel in the middle of the Sister's desk and we'd smile at each other as we watched Sister Mary Agnes, carefully remove it. Her expression of disgust told us the prank was working and each week Joey seemed to find something messier than the week before. Joey loved making life difficult for Sister Mary Agnes and the whole class enjoyed watching.

Perhaps the most tense exchange between Joey and Sister Mary Agnes was during one of our religion classes. Sister Mary Agnes was talking about the Virgin Mary when Joey piped up with, "Really Sister, are you sure she was a virgin?"

"Yes, I'm sure, Joey, I'm certain she was a virgin," Sister responded in a tone meant to end the conversation. But, Joey wasn't finished.

"Well, my sister's a virgin, too, and her little boy is my brother so maybe----."

With a red face, Sister Mary Agnes quickly cut Joey off.

The Sunny Side of Crazy

"Class, take your English books out, You have an assignment for tomorrow."

After school, I asked Joey if it was true. She looked at me as if she was surprised I didn't know. "Why do you think my mother is sending me to an all-girls high school?" she asked.

Summer arrived before we were ready for it. Joey and I spent as much time as we could together and that included a lot of sleepovers. Twice a week, Captain Cindy would pick me up for my first job as her helper at the community pool. Most local teens hung out there trying to impress each other. That's where I learned how boys and girls flirt and how to do it. It was something I wasn't ready for, but my secret friend Skye was, and she was more than happy to help

At first, I wore slacks and polo shirts to the pool because I didn't dare wear anything else. But, by the end of the summer, I was in skimpy shorts or a bathing suit. Outfits that Captain Cindy repeatedly told me were inappropriate. I didn't care. I didn't want to be her helper anyway.

Once in a while, Captain Cindy would catch me helping a boy or girl sneak in. She said it could get her fired and it was my job to keep an eye on everyone coming through the gate. If they didn't have a pass or the entrance fee, I was supposed to report them to her immediately. I didn't, and by mid-summer, she caught on and said she couldn't let me help her anymore. It didn't matter, I had made grateful friends, and I learned to flirt.

I spent a lot of time that summer trying to convince Mom to send me to the Catholic high school. I wanted to continue to go to school with Joey, and besides, I knew I wasn't ready for what was ahead.

"No way" was her response. She said she couldn't afford it and that was final! I'd pout and complain.

"Mom, what if everyone hates me?"

"They won't."

"What if C. J. is in one of my classes?"

"You'll survive, Honey, trust me. We all do."

Just before we returned to school, during one of our last sleepovers, Joey's sister came into her bedroom and gave me advice on attending a public high school.

"Forget the popular cliques. They won't want you, and you don't want to be like them."

"Grab a seat in the back of the classes before they're all taken."

"Find someone to eat lunch with asap. You don't want to sit alone."

"Wear pretty underwear. Gym classes are brutal. Girls check each other out."

"Stay in the bathroom only as long as necessary."

"Never have a conversation over a stall wall."

"Don't read what's written on the walls."

"Never snitch; mind your own business"

After that, I didn't want junior high to ever end.

The Sunny Side of Crazy

Eighth grade was a wonderful year. I had a best friend, was accepted by my classmates, and had a teacher who would happily give us all a diploma.

At Saint Mary's no one talked about putting me in a special education class, or sending me to counseling. Thanks to my secret friends, I came across as normal, whereas in reality, I was anything but.

I was becoming more and more dependent on my "friends" to get me through classes and challenges. And, I was becoming more and more forgetful. What I learned in one class I could forget by the next.

I spent more and more time writing in my journals. That's how I tried to figure out what was going on. Many times my friends seemed to know things I didn't. I would read their entries and once in a while even talk to them. When Mom caught me talking to myself, she began to pry. That's when I decided to keep all our communication written in my journals.

Calle and Suki wrote a lot, Sam a little, and even Tin, my terrible twin, added a swear word now and then. Every night after reading and writing I'd hide my journals under my bed until they were full and then transfer them into my "hopeless chest."

I wanted to tell Joey about my special friends. After all, she was very, very smart. I thought maybe she would understand what was happening. But, in the end, I couldn't take the chance. *What if she thought I was crazy?* I couldn't imagine losing the closest friend I'd ever had.

The Sunny Side of Crazy

Ready or not, eighth grade was ending, and we had to go our separate ways.

The summer was a disappointment. Joey was busy with gymnastics and Mom and Captain Cindy planned a "catch up summer." When I complained about the Captain being around so much Mom said, "Well, I can't afford a private high school but at least we can get you ready for where you'll be going. Don't worry, Mikala, everything will be okay. You will do just fine."

"Sure Mom. Whatever you say."

It seemed like everyone was looking forward to high school except for me. For my classmates, it meant freedom, a place to make new friends, meet boys, date, dance, drive, and discover. For me, it meant one more secret to hide. That secret's name was Skye.

During junior high school, I'd become accustomed to Suki stepping in with her love of learning and obsession with numbers to help me with my studies. She was Captain Cindy's prized student and Fu's adored teacher.

And, I depended on Calle, who popped in with her wild sense of humor and contagious laugh to entertain my classmates and irritate Sister Mary Agnes. I don't think Sam ever entered a classroom. After all, what Sam wanted was Mom's love, attention, and approval at home. Skye's intrusion wasn't clear. She was vain, competitive, impatient and daring; everything I wasn't. I hated looking in mirrors, but Skye liked it. She loved what she saw looking back at her and became absolutely obsessed with cosmetics and edgy clothes.

The Sunny Side of Crazy

I knew it was going to be difficult to keep my newest friend a secret. Mom told me she didn't like my "new attitude" and I didn't care. The fact was, I was impressed with Skye and looked forward to reading her comments in my journals.

CHAPTER 12
HIGH SCHOOL HEADACHES

At exactly 8:15 on the first day of high school, I stood in front of locker 127 sweating bullets. I'd been dreading this moment all summer. Mom bought me a combination lock early that summer so I'd have plenty of time to practice. I tried opening and closing it over and over again but it was impossible! Remembering the combination was easy but turning the dial just right was beyond me. By mid-summer I'd given up.

Now, here I was, facing locker 127, knowing, I had no idea how I was going to lock and unlock it in time to make classes. I opened my backpack and pulled out the lock. *What if I'm late? I can't tell the teacher I can't open a lock. What if other students see me struggling and laugh? What if I just leave it unlocked? What if something gets stolen? Like what? A sweater? Candy bar? So what? I can live with that!* My thoughts were interrupted by the sound of the bell.

I made my decision and turned down the hall toward English 101. I felt nothing but relief as I dropped the lock in a garbage bin.

My first class went fine. A few girls from grade school smiled and said, "Hi."

I wondered if I had changed as much as they had.

My second class finished early. Mr. Jacobs handed us a bunch of papers and rambled on about how difficult freshman year would be. He wanted us to know his door was always open.

The Sunny Side of Crazy

As I made my way to the cafeteria for lunch, I thought about what Joey's sister had said. "You never want to sit at a table alone. That can be the kiss of death for a freshman. Find someone to eat with asap.

I made my way through the food line thinking about how to cheerfully say, "Mind if I sit with you?" but then, a voice broke through. It was Melody. "Hey Miki, do you want to sit with us? " *Us? Was she inviting me to sit with a group? Was it going to be that easy?*

"Sure, why not?" I replied as casually as I could fake.

Relieved, I sat quietly listening to classmates share their summer stories and high school fears. Lunch periods were short and there was still plenty left to talk about when the bell rang. That's when I heard the most wonderful words of the day.

"Hey, Miki, tomorrow tell us about your summer. Same place, same time, Okay?"

Okay? Was it ever! I'd found my place. I was accepted.

I hung out with this group of girls throughout my high school years. They were nice, solid, academically strong and a lot of fun.

On the first day, I also ran into C.J., the bully. He was on my "worry list" but needn't have been. He smiled and called out "Hey, Miki, Good to see you girl, how are you?" as if we were old friends.

At first, I couldn't believe it was him. He must have spent another whole summer eating ding dongs. And, to say he was going through a major breakout would be kind.

"Hey CJ, good to see you," I lied.

"Yeah, maybe we can get together some time," he responded.

"Yeah, sure," I lied, making a conscious decision to avoid him at all costs.

My friend Calle was disappointed. She'd found him a worthy playmate, but this was high school, and who I was seen with mattered.

I went home the first day anxious to call Joey and tell her I'd followed her sister's advice and nothing was as bad as expected. I wanted to tell her how good it felt when I dropped the lock in the garbage, and because gym was my last class, the girls were in too much of a hurry to check out each other's underwear.

All in all, the first day of high school was a success. In fact, freshman year was pretty good. I depended on Suki's smarts to help me through classes and Calle for fun.

At the beginning of the year, keeping my special friends a secret wasn't really a problem. But, as the year wore on, everyone saw more and more of Skye. My forgetfulness increased as my control over my secret friends decreased.

Skye was active and constantly distracted by boys. One of them could have spelled big trouble if Mom hadn't intervened.

She'd left work early, picked up Fu, and was headed home to take us out to celebrate her new promotion. Just as she turned the last corner to our home she noticed two teenagers engaged in a passionate embrace. I was one of them.

The Sunny Side of Crazy

At first, she drove right past, thinking I couldn't be "that girl." I wasn't. It was Skye, someone Mom was about to see a whole lot more of. Mom drove around the block, stopped at the curb and got out. Too engaged to notice, I felt Mom's grasp. "Mikala, get into the car!" she shouted. Instead of dinner, I got an "it will never happen again" lecture. Then she called the boy's mother. I lost that boyfriend but there were plenty more to come.

Freshman year passed quickly. The Captain was still coming around to help me with whatever she thought I needed. I found her concern and dedication extremely annoying. Especially during summers when I joined my friends at the community pool.

She didn't approve of my swimsuits, the guys that looked at me from across the pool, or the way I smiled back at them. She would stroll into my little group of girlfriends during her breaks as if she were invited. "Are you kids having a good time," she'd ask. We would assure her we were having a blast and wait for her to leave so we could resume our conversations. It was amazing how long she could stand there waiting before she realized we were not going to include her. Eventually, she would say, "Well, I'd better get back to work." We'd breathe a sigh of relief and wait until she was out of hearing range before giggling and returned to the gossip of the day.

During my junior year, I got a job at the new drug store in town. I saved every penny for my rare shopping days with my old friend, Joey. Our time together was limited. She was enrolled in a special gymnastics class, and I was busy working. Still, time together was special. We both knew we would soon be going separate ways. She would be going away to college and I would, be going, well I didn't know. College wasn't on my agenda, and I didn't have any idea what was.

I hung out with the same crowd all four years. Skye never missed a dance and thanks to my other friends, and yes, even the Captain, I managed to graduate without falling victim to the dangers some other classmates had.

Fortunately, I had wonderful teachers. Many recognized I was different, but no one could quite understand exactly how or why. Realizing I was trying my best and, at times, even showing a little brilliance, a few teachers gave me extra time on tests and assignments. By the end of high school, I'd made the first chair in band, submitted drawings for art shows and even submitted an article to the school publication. Band was hard. Mr. Stoffer was exactly the kind of teacher Joey's sister had warned me about. He loved popular and talented kids. I was neither, but Skye was and she hated the way he catered to a few and ignored the rest.

Once in a while, he'd ask me to play something alone. Often, Skye would play perfectly. Unfortunately, I didn't. Mr. Stoffer would say "Mikala, you are truly the most inconsistent player I've ever heard."

At night, I'd pour my feelings into the growing number of journals I kept hidden in my closet. Sometimes I wrote for hours, and I think I spent as much time reading the entries from my secret friends. They wrote about some things I knew about and things I knew nothing about. I found it fascinating and a little frightening. Who were these secret friends? I had no idea. I was pretty sure they weren't the silly angels Mom talked about when I was a kid, or lingering imaginary playmates. Well, whoever, they were, I thought of them as more than secrets. They truly were my friends.

By the end of my senior year, most of my classmate's conversations had turned to colleges, future plans and boyfriends. I didn't have plans or a serious boyfriend, and Mom didn't think I was ready for college. She encouraged me to sign up for classes at our local junior college. No one I knew was going there, so I refused. Everyone was going somewhere, except me. I didn't think I was going anywhere.

But Mom had a surprise for me. I was going somewhere after all. Mom was moving our family south shortly after graduation. She called it "good news!"

She would be trading snow for warm weather, and I would be trading the known for the unknown. And, as if that wasn't enough, another new little sister would soon be joining our family. I was beyond angry and I showed it.

Mom said I had a bad attitude and so did my teachers. Every few days she got a call about my disruptive behavior. "It just isn't like her," they would say. It wasn't. I threw my classmate's books off his desk for no apparent reason. At my final band concert, I saw a boy sitting in the first chair. I was supposed to sit there so I pushed him. I pushed so hard, the whole chair fell over and as his ass hit the floor, the entire band broke out laughing. That was my last concert.

By then, I was no longer the daughter Mom knew. I was her adversary, and I was going to make our move as difficult as possible.

CHAPTER 13
THROUGH A MOTHER'S EYES

I can't take more winters here in Michigan.. I've always wanted to live in a warmer climate and finally have the opportunity. I can keep my job and work from home. How can I possibly pass up this opportunity? I doubt I'll ever have another chance like this. I won't say no just because Mikala doesn't want to move.

I know Miki's pissed, but to tell the truth, I'm beyond caring. I also know she's going to punish me. She's good at that. She'll ignore me, become passive-aggressive, or start arguments about anything and everything. She thinks the whole world should revolve around her, and her moodiness is driving me crazy. I thought at some point she would grow out of it, but that's not happening. She's more self-absorbed and selfish than ever. She doesn't seem capable of thinking of anyone but herself.

I've tried to talk to her but it's absolutely exhausting. She jumps from one topic to another so quickly I can rarely figure out what she's trying to say. By the time we finish talking, I've often forgotten what my point was in the first place.

She used to be such a sweet little girl, trying so hard to please, Now, she's a different child. I'm spending so much of my time and energy on her issues, I'm neglecting everyone else. The truth is, I'm tired. It's time to focus on the rest of the family.

The Sunny Side of Crazy

Her lying and blaming is just too much. I don't know who she is anymore. The teen years with her older sister were challenging but nothing like this.

Well, bottom line, we are moving to a warmer climate, and she'll have to deal with it.

We've gotten through tough times before, and we'll get through these.

PART 3
Hidden Dangers

The Sunny Side of Crazy

CHAPTER 14

GOING SOUTH

Everyone who knows Mom gets nervous when they hear her say, "I've got some good news!" The day Mom told me we were moving south, I was in a state of shock and as angry as on that day a few weeks before, when she told me I was going to have another little sister. What? Another little sister. Why? How could she disrupt my life again.? Did I want another sister? No! Did I want to move south? No! Did I have a choice? No. Of course not. I never did! When she told me about another adoption, I walked out of the room while she was still talking.

Going south was a wonderful opportunity, she said. I'll work from home, be closer to the ocean, no more shoveling snow. Another little sister would be good for Fu and complete our little family. Blah, blah, blah, on and on she went, not noticing when I left.

Yeah "Blah, blah, blah."

Who cared? I couldn't listen to it anymore. She knew I hated change!

I'd graduated from high school, found my first full-time job, and had a routine. I knew what the next day would bring, and the next and the next. And now, she wanted me to start all over with another new little sister in some god-forsaken place called South Carolina.

I sat down on my bed, grabbed my journal, and indulged in self-pity. I complained to my secret friends. Sam tried to comfort me. Tin swore, Suki and Calle pouted and Skye wrote that she really didn't give a damn.

That night, I told Mom I wasn't feeling well and couldn't eat dinner. She didn't buy that for a minute. It wasn't the first time I'd refused to eat as a way of expressing my anger. Mom wasn't having any more of it.

"Miki, you're too old for this. I shouldn't have to sit next to you to make sure you eat."

Ten minutes later I'd eaten a few bites, Mom left the room and the dogs happily ate the rest.

I tried to block the move and the new sister out of my mind, but it was impossible! Mom spent all her time preparing for garage sales and getting ready for the next child. I spent my free time babysitting Fu and encouraging her to resist the move in whatever way she could.

We competed for Mom's time and attention and then bonded together in making the move more difficult. My secret friends continued to play their parts and grew stronger with each appearance. Even Tin, the elusive evil one, showed up more than once.

One day Mom told me to "man our table" at the neighbor's garage sale. I was already pissed and in a foul mood. An hour into the sale, C.J.'s mother showed up. Before I knew it, I was shouting and swearing at her about her dumb ass, bully of a son.

I don't know exactly what words were spoken, but it was enough to make C.J.'s Mother furious. With a bright red face, she headed directly to our neighbor's table and started yelling at her. The neighbor motioned for me to go home, and in less than the two minutes it took to get there, they'd already called Mom. Mom grounded me. Fu didn't speak to me for days, and I never understood why.

Eventually, whatever happened was forgotten and we (including the new sister) were packed and ready to go. Mom, Fu, Kati, two dogs and me all in one car. My older sister, my brother-in-law, nephew, niece, baby and their dog in the other! On the long drive down to South Carolina, Mom shared another surprise, my brother-in-law's new job wouldn't start for another month, and until then, we would all be living together. I would be the babysitter. By the time we arrived in the South, I was all "surprised out."

Two days before Christmas, we walked into our new home. There was no snow outside and no Christmas tree inside. Mom was angry because the furniture hadn't arrived, my nephew was crying because he didn't think Santa could find us. Fu and I were fighting about who would get which bedroom. Meanwhile, my older sister was busy changing extremely smelly diapers on a screaming baby, and my impatient brother-in-law was cursing at the dogs while unloading the cars.

By nightfall, we were all exhausted and fell asleep on mattresses spread around the living room floor. There wasn't a bit of Christmas spirit in sight.

But, when the sun came up the following morning, everything changed. I woke up to see my five-year-old nephew, Kyle staring out the window.

"What's up Kyle?"

"Miki, quiet, come here, hurry, come here," he whispered. I climbed over Fu and Kati to join him at the window. There, in our new front yard was a family of deer munching away at our bushes. Kyle looked up at me with a beautiful smile and whispered, "Aunt Miki, Santa is going to find us after all, isn't he?"

"Yes, I guess he already has," I whispered back.

The second day in our new home was much better. The furniture arrived, beds were put together and Mom stocked the refrigerator. Fu told me she found boxes of presents hidden in the garage. That was another of her many gifts; she could find almost anything hidden anywhere, except my journals, which I hid with the greatest of care.

My brother-in-law went searching for a Christmas tree, found the last one on the lot, and we filled its scrawny branches with white lights and little red velvet bows. It was one of the prettiest Christmas trees we ever had.

Early Christmas morning, we woke up to the smell of warm Christmas foods from the local grocery store and an abundance of presents under the tree. Christmas carols were playing on Mom's new stereo and everything was perfect. The family ate, played and ate some more. I don't think any of us fought. I don't even remember the baby crying.

After the second round of dessert, my temporary roommates, Fu and Kati, and I picked up our shiny new journals and headed to my bedroom. Fu and Kati fell asleep while I was still writing. I carefully hid my diary under my mattress. I knew Kati couldn't read English and was pretty sure Fu couldn't read my writing, but I wasn't taking any chances. Christmas day was fun but didn't last long enough.

The rest of the week was spent unpacking, exploring and arguing over who got to use which bathroom first. I indulged in long periods of self-pity and of course, blamed Mom for turning my life upside down. Everything that was wrong was her fault. And, believe me, I found plenty wrong.

Our new house was in total chaos. Mom set up a temporary office in her bedroom. My sister and brother-in-law started house hunting. Fu and Kati prepared for their new school, and I pouted while changing lots of poopy diapers. Mom didn't seem to notice or care how unhappy I was. At night I'd brood and complain to Sam about how miserable my life had become.

He'd tell me, "It's okay to cry, Miki. You know we're safe now, you can tell Mom you're angry." *Impossible,* I thought.

Instead, I did what I always did: I pretended everything was okay and made Mom's life miserable. I'd agree to do something, and then purposely do it wrong, or insist I'd forgotten. I'd pretend to eat, throw my food in the garbage and say it was good.

My desire to lose weight and see a double-digit number on the scale returned in full force, and I set my new goal at 80 pounds. I stopped eating until the night Mom finally found time to prepare a homemade meal. We'd been eating fast food for days, and all of us were relieved to see her in the kitchen. Fu and Kati practically attacked the meatloaf, mashed potatoes and vegetables. I took one look and ran for the bathroom.

The Sunny Side of Crazy

The smell and sight made me sick, real sick. As I cleaned up, I looked up and saw Mom's reflection in the mirror. She was looking at me with an expression of pure disgust!

She went back to the dining room, and I went to bed hoping she wouldn't come in to talk or say goodnight. She didn't, but the next morning she was sitting at the breakfast table waiting for me. She watched as I took a couple of bites of toast. Luckily, my sister interrupted, and by the time she returned, the rest of my toast was history in the bottom of the garbage can.

"Mom, we've got to hurry. I need to be at my interview in fifteen minutes."

I jumped up and ran outside. Mom followed me to the car.

"Miki, you know we need to talk. We can't let this get out of hand again."

"Yeah, I know; I know Mom. Later okay? After the interview!"

Ten minutes later Mom dropped me off in front of a drug store three miles from home.

"Aren't you going to wish me luck?" I asked as I jumped out of the car.

"Good luck, Miki," she replied without as much as a smile.

My interview for the clerk's position went well. I knew I could do the job but was worried about the interview. I shouldn't have been. The manager talked on and on about the store, the staff and his goals. He barely glanced at my reference letter and when he did, he only asked one question.

The Sunny Side of Crazy

"Why do you want the job?"

I don't remember what I said, but it must have been what he wanted to hear because he hired me on the spot.

"Can you start on Monday?"

"Sure," I replied, happy to be giving up free babysitting. My mood improved immediately. The interview was so much easier than I'd expected.

"Mom, I got the job!" I shouted as I climbed back into the car. She closed her book and put the key in the ignition.

"Miki, I'm worried."

I cut her off immediately,

"Mom, not now, please. I got the job. Can't you just be happy for me? The holidays are almost over, don't spoil them."

Always one to get the last word, Mom looked at me and said, "Miki, the New Year is going to be different, very different." She was right; it was.

The Sunny Side of Crazy

CHAPTER 15

MY GOLDEN WEEK

For me, the week after Christmas was golden. I was only on the job a few days when Shari walked in. She was young, about my age and very attractive. My special friend Skye was impressed.

"Hi, can I help you find something?"

"No, I'll find it. I know where everything is. Are you new here?"

"I just started this week, but I've worked with cosmetics for a long time. If you have any questions, I'll be glad to answer them."

She narrowed her eyes as if she was scrutinizing me. Then, she laughed. "It's about time they got someone in here who knows something."

I took a deep breath and tried again.

"We have some new lipsticks. The colors are cool. Want to see them?"

"Why not? By the way, my name's Shari."

"I'm Mikala, but my friends call me Miki."

"Okay, Miki, show me what you've got."

For the next fifteen minutes, we bonded over scents, colors and creams. We had a lot in common. We both loved cosmetics, clothes and reality shows. Still, I was surprised when Shari looked at me and said, "Hey, let's hang out sometime."

"Yeah, I'd like that."

"Great, I'll stop by next week, and we can set something up."

That alone would have made my week golden, but something even more significant happened.

On the same day, just as I was about to end my shift, an attractive, elegantly dressed woman walked directly up to my counter.

"Excuse me, I haven't seen you here before. Are you from China?"

For a moment, I didn't know what to say. I'd never been mistaken for Chinese before and her boldness surprised me.

"I'm not Chinese, I'm from Japan."

"Oh, now that is interesting. Are you a student?"

"No, I work here."

"Really? I thought you might be one of my new students. I'm Professor Grander. I teach psychology at the campus across the street. And you are?"

"I'm Miki. Can I help you find something?"

"No, I have what I need here."

She set several high-end creams on my counter and watched me intently as I rang up her purchase.

The Sunny Side of Crazy

"Here's your receipt and thank you," I said.

The professor's eyes narrowed, "I'm sorry, could you speak louder, I didn't hear you."

I was sure she had but embarrassed I said, "Thank you. Please come again."

She smiled, nodded, and began to walk away. Then suddenly, she turned around and returned to my counter.

"If you do enroll in classes, please stop in and see me. I counsel many of the foreign students, and I'm sure they'd love to meet you."

"Thanks, I will."

I watched her walk away and thought about how impressed Mom would be to hear there was a university campus so close, and I'd been mistaken for a student. *What a great first day!* I felt like I was walking on air. When I left, Mom was waiting, as promised, in the parking lot.

"Mom, you won't believe what happened today," I gushed as I got in the car. "I just met a professor from the campus across the street, and she said if I become a student, I should come and see her."

That was all Mom needed to hear.

"I didn't know there was a campus so close. Let's drive over and take a look."

Before I could object, Mom was driving across the street and entering the campus. She stopped directly in front of a large stately looking building.

"Come on Mikii, let's go in."

"Mom, you can't park here."

"I'll only be here for a couple of minutes," she said, as she got out of the car. Twenty minutes later she returned waving brochures over her head.

"Miki, guess what, there's still time for you to enroll. You'd be on probationary status until your transcripts come in, but there's still time to enroll!" I didn't say a word but Mom smiled all the way home.

Once home, Mom started in. I knew she wouldn't let the eating issue go. She didn't.

"Come in the kitchen, Miki. I need some tea."

When Mom said she needed tea, we knew a serious discussion would soon follow. I tried desperately to distract her.

"I think I made a friend today, Mom. Her name is Shari and she wants to hang out."

"Hang out where?" Mom asked.

"I don't know; go to a movie, have dinner, whatever. You know what I mean."

"No, I don't Miki. We just moved here. I'd like to meet her before you hang out."

"MOM!"

"Does she drive?"

"Yeah Mom, she drives like most kids my age do."

The Sunny Side of Crazy

"I need to meet her first, Miki."

Mom carried a pot of tea and two cups to the table. Damn, I knew *the only time mom made a whole pot was when she was expecting a long conversation.* I remained quiet as she went through her private tea ceremony. Her tea had to be a particular color with exactly an ounce of cream and two teaspoons of sugar. I knew I'd have to wait for her to finish, or she'd start all over again. Once her tea was perfect, I waited for her to take her first sip. This time, she spoke before taking it.

"Miki, I don't have time to sit with you at every meal like I did when you were young. So, here's the deal: every Sunday, we will have a weigh-in. If you lose more weight you will quit your job and not get your driver's license until you have put the weight back on plus an extra pound."

"WHAT? Mom, you promised after we got here---! "

"And, you promised you would eat! We're not going through this again. So, let me be clear, no job, no driver's license, no outings. You will go back to therapy, and if necessary, into the hospital."

I sat there in shock. I'd seen Mom angry many times but this was more than anger, this was pure determination.

"It isn't as easy as you think!"

"I didn't say it would be easy. I said I will do whatever I have to do. Do you understand me?"

I nodded, left the room, and as so often before, said to myself, *"She sure knows how to spoil a perfect day,"*

The Sunny Side of Crazy

That night I found a list of Mom's rules for driving lying on my bed.

You will be responsible for paying your own insurance.

1. No drinking period (you already know that).

2. For the first six months, you will drive alone

3. You will let me know where you're going and when you'll get back

4. You will keep the car clean

In the event you break this contract, your driving privileges will be suspended. And, of course, as with all Mom's contracts, she left room for my signature. I signed it and left it in the middle of her bed.

CHAPTER 16
STORM BREWING

Less than a week later, I was enrolled in Dr. Grander's psychology class and our whole family was looking forward to the New Year —a new start for all of us. I thought it was going to be my year, as my new friend, Shari said, "A year to grow up and move ahead." After all, I had a job, a friend, and I was going to be a university student with a professor taking me under her wing. And, best of all, I was going to get my driver's license.

I studied the driver's manual night and day and forced myself to eat whatever fricking junk food I could for days before my weigh-ins. Shari and my secret friend Skye thought I was ready for anything and everything. I agreed, completely.

Trying to hide my embarrassment, I told Shari that my Mom insisted on meeting her before we could get together.

"Mom wants to meet you before we hang out, I mean because we're new in the neighborhood and all."

Shari squinched up her face, rolled her eyes, and laughed. "Are you kidding Miki? Time for you to grow up, girl; you've got to get yourself a life!"

The following Sunday, Shari came for dinner. I could tell from the moment she walked in that Mom wouldn't be impressed, and I was right!. I thought it might be her tight mini skirt, or the throng that peeked out when she leaned over but Mom didn't say anything about those things. She said, "Shari's background doesn't make sense. She travels, drives a new car, and eats at expensive restaurants, all on a clerk's salary?"

"Mom, you can't hold hard work against her," I said.

"Miki, what she told me about her family doesn't make sense; it doesn't add up. Something's off! I'm not sure what, but something's wrong with this picture." Mom exclaimed.

She trusted her gut feelings on everything.

"Mom," I said defiantly, "I'm going to hang out with Shari."

I expected her to respond in kind, but instead, she mumbled "Whatever," and walked out of the room. That night I started a new journal in which I listed all the "get a life" experiences I wanted to have. I had high expectations and was determined to grow up fast.

By the end of January, I'd passed my driver's test, was an enrolled university student and had gained three pounds. Eating was by far the hardest of the three. Every bite stuck in my throat. I choked, gagged and puked, but forced in enough to gain weight. Mom kept her end of the bargain and had taken me for my driving test. Two hours later, I had already broken rule number two.

Determined to take my first solo drive, I picked up the car keys and one of our dogs for companionship. After all, what trouble could one four-legged passenger cause? The answer, plenty! As I gripped the wheel to turn the first corner, Rebel jumped in my lap and let out a loud bark. That's all it took. I swerved. "Shit!"

The Sunny Side of Crazy

I'd run into the neighbor's mailbox. I prayed the damage wouldn't be noticeable but as soon as I got out of the car, I found God wasn't on my side. Not only was the smashed mailbox lying close to the middle of the road, but there was a deep, dark, gash all down the side of Mom's car.

Of course, she was furious, and by the end of my first driving day, my privileges were suspended, my salary attached, and I was grounded. Mom drove me back and forth to work and classes, complaining each and every day.

Even with my secret friends helping me, I was having trouble keeping up my grades in psychology. Dr. Grander noticed and suggested a solution.

"Mikala, you're struggling, and I know you need help. I'm a therapist, as well as a professor, and if you'd like, I can help you with your studies and adjusting to university life. Since you are my student, my rate would be very reasonable."

I wasn't at all sure what Dr. Grander was offering, but I knew Mom was as big a fan of therapy as higher education. That night I told her about the professor's offer.

"Do you mean she wants to tutor you?"

"Well, she said she wants to help me. She's a therapist and a professor, so I guess she can help me with a lot of things."

"Did she say how much she would charge?"

"She said she would give me a special student rate. I'm not sure exactly."

"If you think she can help, find out her rates, where and when. Then we can talk about it."

After my next class, I followed Dr. Grander to her office and asked her Mom's questions.

As soon as I got home, I shared the answers. We would meet at Dr. Grander's home for an hour on Saturday mornings. She would charge half what Mom had previously paid for therapy.

"I've never heard of anything like this but I don't think it can do any harm. Do you, Miki?"

"What harm could it do Mom?"

The correct answer turned out to be plenty.

For a couple of months everything seemed to be going well. At work, my manager showed great patience. Over and over, I'd heard him say, "You can do it, Mikala, let's just go over it one more time." One more time became a dozen, but he never complained.

The month passed quickly, and I got back on the road, had my own spending money, and was hanging out with Shari and her friends. I was growing up! We spent hours every weekend hanging out at the mall, or watching steamy movies at her apartment.

During Saturday sessions, in what Dr. Grander referred to as therapy, I was hearing exactly what I wanted to hear. It was time for me to grow up, and Mom was being overprotective! I enjoyed complaining about Mom, and Dr. Grander seemed to enjoy listening. At times, Mom asked why I was spending so much time with Shari and questioned the appropriateness of Dr. Grander's many gifts.

"Miki, I'm sure there are others who need your professor's old tight clothes more than you do. Why don't you tell her that?"

"Okay, I will," I lied.

"Miki, don't you think you should spend a little more time at home and a little less time with Shari?"

"I will soon. Shari's introducing me to kids my age," I'd reply, without telling her how much older her friends really were.

Then, I'd add, "Maybe I don't need to go to therapy anymore. I'd have more time at home."

Mom would immediately back off. After years of struggling to get me to stay in therapy, she had no intention of blowing it.

The truth was, I was uncomfortable with Dr. Grander's therapy. She was constantly asking questions about Mom and my sisters. I knew she showed more interest in my family than previous therapists, but I liked to complain, and she let me. She also approved of my friendship with Shari and encouraged me to spread my wings. That's exactly what I wanted to hear.

Dr. Grander made it clear she saw my mom as overprotective, unreasonable and an obstacle to my normal development. By the end of January, she was encouraging me to accompany Shari on one of her weekend trips to Florida.

"I can't imagine why your mother won't let you go. It's not unusual for people your age to go on trips together."

That was all I needed to hear.

"Mom, even Dr. Grander thinks I should go. She thinks you're being unreasonable and says you shouldn't treat me like a child."

"Maybe she doesn't know you as well as I do Miki. You are young for your age."

"Come on Mom, you have always said I should listen to my therapist. Now I'm listening."

Against Mom's better judgment, the next weekend I was on my way to St. Petersburg with Shari. As we passed Orlando, I suggested we stop at Disney on our way home. Shari burst out laughing,

"No! That's a trip to take with your mommy," she replied.

"Only joking," I lied.

We arrived at our Holiday Inn just before nine that night, checked in, ate and met up with Shari's friends. That was the first of my surprises. Instead of jeans and T-shirts, they were all dressed in short, tight evening wear. I had only brought jeans and a bathing suit. That's all Shari told me to bring. Besides, I didn't even own anything like they were wearing.

When we got to our room, Shari quickly changed outfits.

"Hey, Miki, if you'd like to go out with us you can borrow something. But, we're not coming back until pretty late, maybe two or three!"

Sensing the insincerity of the invitation, I told her what she wanted to hear. "I'm kinda pooped. I'll pass."

"You sure? Okay, but I brought extras."

Embarrassed, I again declined and flipped on the TV. I didn't want to think about being left out but I knew I was. Not telling me to bring evening clothes wasn't an oversight. Shari knew they were going out and didn't want me tagging along.

"How do I look, Miki?"

"You look sexy, Shari, real sexy."

"See you later."

"Yeah, enjoy," I said in as cheerful a voice as I could fake. Feeling let down, I told myself our fun would start in the morning.

When I woke up at seven, Shari still hadn't returned. Disappointed, I made my way to the breakfast buffet and played with some food as I tried to convince myself there was still time for fun.

I returned to our room an hour later to find Shari sleeping soundly in the same clothes she'd worn out. Quietly, I slipped on my swimsuit and headed to the pool. So far the trip was a bummer, and we only had the afternoon to turn it around. Hours later, Shari walked up to my lounge chair.

"Hey Miki, I've been looking all over for you. Come on, hurry, we need to get going."

Still pissed off, I grumbled, "What's the hurry, Shari? The mall is open until ten, isn't it?"

"Come on, come on, come on," she replied.

I grabbed my towel, returned to our room, and slipped into my jeans. All the while giving myself a pep talk. *At least we were going to spend the afternoon together.*

"You're going to love this," she screamed as we pulled up in front of a dumpy strip mall. Before I could ask what the heck we were doing there, Shari was pushing me into the back room of a photographer's studio, where we were greeted by a man who looked more like a bodybuilder than a photographer.

"Long time, no see my love," he said as he gave Shari a powerful bear hug.

"And, who is your little friend?

"Her name is Miki," Shari shouted as she dragged me into a huge concrete dressing room.

The room was overflowing with clothes.

"Grab something, Miki!"

I pulled a vintage black dress from a rack and turned around for Shari's approval.

Shari was just sliding out of her jeans.

"Shari, what the heck?" She was standing there buck naked. She hadn't even worn underwear! She laughed and narrowed her eyes. I quickly looked away.

"Miki, what the hell?" she echoed back as she pulled an American flag from its holder and headed out the door. I didn't know whether to laugh or cry.

Shari was beautiful even naked, but the lingering smell of cigarette smoke and cheap perfume turned my stomach. With laughter drifting from the adjoining room, I switched the vintage black gown for a bright red one and opened the door. Shari was posing with the flag barely covering her boobs and crotch.

She gave me one of her, *oh my God you've got to be kidding looks,* while the photographer stared at me with an amused grin on his face.

"I have a Chinese, Japanese and Korean flag in the closet. Would you like one of them, Darling?"

I'm sure my face turned as red as the dress. I shook my head and sat down to watch Shari finish her shoot. It took a while. Thank God, my own took less than ten minutes. I was relieved and wanted out! The truth was I wanted to go home. Saturday's evening turned out to be a repeat of the night before; the only difference being Shari returned just before check-out time the following day.

We arrived home before ten that night.

"How was the trip, Honey?"

"It was great Mom, It was great."

I didn't show Mom the photos until the next day. First, she looked at the pictures of Shari provocatively draped in the American flag and then at mine "These photos don't look at all like you," was all she said.

The Sunny Side of Crazy

CHAPTER 17
SPINNING OUT OF CONTROL

Spring comes early in the South. Beautiful weather filled with all kinds of activities. For the first time, there wasn't enough time in the day to do all the things I wanted to. When I wasn't working, I was with Shari or Dr. Grander. If this was what being grown-up meant, I wanted more. I spent as little time as possible at home, and for the most part, Mom didn't seem to mind.

She spent her time chauffeuring Fu to play practice and trying to keep track of our new little sister. Kati. Kati was almost seven—smart, strong-willed and a match for Mom in almost every way. Her response to rules and restrictions was to ignore them. She's a "do first and apologize later," kind of kid. Except, well, Kati never apologized, She had survived life on the streets in China and wasn't about to let Mom control her now.

Mom's attention was scattered, and we all took advantage by pushing her rules to the limit. I complained she was too strict, and usually added, that Shari and Dr. Grander agreed.

"You'll be an adult this summer. Then, we can talk about it," Mom said. I didn't think my birthday or summer would ever come, but of course, it did.

My 21st birthday was supposed to be a special day. For the first time, I wouldn't have to celebrate with my family. It took convincing, but Mom finally agreed I was old enough to celebrate with a friend. That was a huge deal because I only had one friend, and Mom didn't like her.

The Sunny Side of Crazy

On the evening of my big day, Shari picked me up, while Mom was reminding me for the umpteenth time there would be no drinking, a 12:30 am curfew and, of course, 911 was just a phone call away.

"Have a good time, Miki," she shouted and waved goodbye.

Feeling exhilarated, I drew in a deep breath of my newfound freedom. It felt wonderful. We were off to who knew where, and I didn't care. Shari and I were laughing at Mom's protectiveness and the unnecessarily concerned expression on her face. A girl's 21st birthday wasn't meant to be spent with a parent, and thank goodness Mom finally understood.

Shari planned the evening, and I assumed we were going to a fancy restaurant, or one of her friend's for a birthday cake, or maybe even a party. An hour later Shari pulled up next to an old dilapidated mobile home.

I was surprised and disappointed. *Maybe we were there to pick up a friend. There had to be a reason. After all, Shari had been talking about my birthday surprise for days.*

As I climbed out of the car, I was assaulted by the sound of a blasting TV. I hesitated, and Shari quickly walked up next to me, put her hand on my shoulder, and whispered, "Don't be a chicken, Miki; we're here to celebrate." She nudged me forward toward the trailer door, where a tipsy-looking old man stood holding it open.

All my senses told me not to take another step, but I was with Shari, my best friend, and I trusted her. I desperately wanted to impress her, to show her I could be just as cool. *How*

130

The Sunny Side of Crazy

could I disappoint the one friend who made me feel normal? She was the one person who had a car and was willing to take me places and show me new things. We had so much fun together. I was being silly, childish. There must be a good reason for stopping here.

I was so focused on pleasing Shari, I ignored my instincts. I hesitated again at the doorway, took a deep breath and walked in.

The man was now standing just inside the doorway. He staggered closer to me and swung his arm around my waist. He pulled me toward him. "So, you're the birthday girl?" he slurred.

His damp shirt and torn jeans reeked of stale beer and old pizza. Overwhelmed by the stench, my stomach lurched, and I began to shake. For the first time in years, I felt as if I were going to blackout. In a low, drunken voice he mumbled, "Don't worry, birthday girl," and then began singing a drunken version of "Happy Birthday." I looked back at Shari who had flopped in front of the TV and was grabbing at a piece of pizza.

I panicked and tried to resist the old man as he pulled me further through the doorway, kicked the door closed and practically drug me into another room. Suddenly, it hit me. Sharon knew exactly what was happening. I'd been set up. This is what she meant by "celebrating my coming of age." Maybe I should have seen this coming. She'd talked endlessly of all her wild sexual adventures. That, she said, was the best part of being an adult.

Holy shit, I'm in trouble now! I barely had time to finish the thought when I felt his putrid hot breath on my mouth and his clumsy hands grabbing my waist. I pushed. But he was strong and determined. I fell backward onto a disheveled bed.

I was trapped, and for a second, I became paralyzed with fear. I could feel myself being overcome by darkness. But, in an instant, a feeling of fearless power, strength and dominance took over. With a rush of energy and control, I kicked. His expression turned to anger. I screamed at the top of my lungs.

"What the fuck do you think you're doing? Get the hell away from me!"

With more strength and speed than I'd ever had, I shoved him aside. A startled, pained expression covered his face as he backed away.

"I'm fucking out of here," I screamed.

Within seconds, I'd raced past Shari, who was still munching pizza and playing with the remote. I jumped into her car, locked the doors and leaned on the horn. Then, I cracked the window open far enough to scream at the top of my lungs, "Shari, get your damn ass out here."

Shari came out, slowly walked to the car, got in and stared at me with an expression I couldn't read.

"What the hell were you thinking, Shari?"

She looked at me as if she wanted to say something but quickly turned her attention to the road. We drove home in silence.

I thought about my snippy response to Mom's innocent question, "*Where are you girls going?*"

The Sunny Side of Crazy

"We're too old to leave breadcrumbs, Mom."

The truth was I had no idea where we were going, and I had no idea where we'd been. Tears began to trickle down my cheeks. *Not so funny now, Miki! Not so funny.*

I'd been betrayed. Mom would be angry. Well, n*o need for her to know. Wrong, no such luck!* When Shari dropped me off in front of the house, the kitchen light was still on. I opened the door, hoping I could make it to my bedroom before Mom noticed me. That didn't happen.

"Miki, come in the kitchen for a minute."

Mom was sitting at the kitchen table drinking tea with a pathetic-looking homemade cake sitting in front of her. I turned away hoping she wouldn't see my tear-streaked face.

"You're home early! How was your evening?" she asked.

"Fine, but I'm tired, I'm going to bed."

"No, Miki! You're not fine. Something's wrong. Look at me, Honey. We need to talk."

"Why?"

"Because I want to know where you were, what happened and why you're crying"

"Mom, it's my birthday. Can't it wait?"

"No, it can't, Honey."

That's all I needed to hear. I couldn't help myself. I opened my mouth, and it all tumbled out. I told her everything that happened from the moment I left the house until I'd returned.

When I finished, I sat silently waiting for her to explode. I expected her to tell me how irresponsible I'd been. How no one knew where I was, and, of course, how I could have been killed.

But Mom didn't say a word. She looked like she was going to cry, stood up and walked out of the room. I felt I was betrayed by my best friend, and now, abandoned by my mom on my birthday too. *Sure, I'd fucked up, but this was supposed to be my day!*

I looked at the lopsided cake in the middle of the table. Next to it were bright paper plates, birthday napkins and an unopened card with my name on it. A wave of nausea overtook me, and I made a mad dash for the bathroom. I held my aching ribs as I puked into the toilet. Feeling weak and miserable, I cleaned up and stumbled to bed. Nothing more was said about that night. Everyone acted as if I hadn't had a birthday. Weeks later Shari started hanging around the store trying to apologize.

"Sorry, Miki. It was just a joke. I didn't expect anything bad to happen."

"Shari, Mom doesn't think I should spend time with you right now."

"Are you saying you're not going to see me anymore because your mommy won't let you?"

Shari began to howl with laughter. "Girl, you are too much!"

That was the last time I saw her.

Soon, I was busy with class, therapy and Dr. Grander. The weather was warm, and it was time for Dr. Grander's pool parties to begin. She invited most of the International students to attend, and she always invited me.

She often asked me to bring my two little sisters along. I said I would, but I never did.

Dr. Grander was my teacher and therapist, and I had no intention of sharing her.

Eventually, Dr. Grander called Mom directly to invite my sisters. She had a party scheduled for Mother's Day. Mom was not pleased, but Dr. Grander stressed the party was for foreign students far away from their homes. Many would be Chinese and Dr. Grander told Mom it would be a wonderful opportunity for Fu and Kati to visit with students from their homeland.

As disappointed as Mom was, and as pissed off as I was, my sisters begged to go. They could hardly control their excitement. Of course, we all knew we should spend the day with Mom, but the temptation was too great. By the time we got home from the party, we had all forgotten about Mother's Day.

We babbled on and on about how wonderful the party was and what a great hostess Dr. Grander was. Just as we were about to go to bed, Fu let out a loud "Oh guys, we forgot to give Mom her presents." We called Mom into the kitchen and pretended we remembered the day and the cake in the fridge. But, we couldn't miss seeing the hurt in her eyes. Mom knew we'd forgotten what was supposed to be her day

A few weeks later, Dr. Grander called Mom again. This time she asked if she would let my sisters accompany me to my next therapy session. Mom was hesitant, and I was angry.

"Whatever for?" Mom asked.

"Mikala is my patient and relationships within the family are important. I'd just like to have one session together."

Reluctantly, Mom agreed. "Miki, I don't understand why Dr. Grander wants the girls to accompany you to therapy. Do you?"

"No," I lied.

But, I did know. I'd complained a lot about my sisters in every session, perhaps exaggerating more than a little. I was angry at Dr. Grander for inviting them and at Mom for allowing them to go. *Wasn't it bad enough that Dr. Grander invited them to her party? Now, she wanted them to come to one of my sessions?*

On the day of the session, I was jealous and in a foul mood. During the session, Kati snuggled next to Dr. Grander and interrupted every time I tried to talk. Dr. Grander's response was to turn her attention away from me and onto Kati. Fu, in turn, expressed her disgust with both of us. While she loved Dr. Grander's party, she was not at all interested in attending a therapy session. She ignored all of the doctor's questions.

When Mom picked us up, Kati was hanging on to Dr. Grander's arm laughing. I was crying, and Fu was ignoring us.

"What's wrong guys?" Mom asked.

"Oh, they're fine," Dr. Grander replied for us, " I'll call you later."

And she did, that very evening,

Uncle Mike had arrived from Michigan earlier that day. We hadn't seen him since moving and Mom was dressed up for a special night out. No longer dressed in jeans and a shirt, she looked beautiful and happier than we had seen her in a long time. She was jabbering about life in the South and Uncle Mike was laughing right along with her. Just as they were about to leave, the phone rang.

I picked up the receiver and froze when I heard the voice. "Can I talk to your mother?" asked Dr. Grander. Reluctantly, I handed Mom the phone. At first, I wondered if the doctor was still on the line. It seemed like Mom was silent for a very long time. Finally...

"No, that's not true," Mom said.

More Silence!

"They most certainly don't hate each other. They're sisters, they fight."

Then, I knew for sure Dr. Grander was telling Mom about our session. For a few more minutes, Mom listened in silence. Then, in a trembling voice, I had never heard before, she said,

"I don't care what you think! They don't have a poisonous relationship with each other, and there is no cancer growing in this family!"

Mom was shaking when she slammed the phone down. Without looking at anyone she headed to her bedroom and started sobbing. Uncle Mike followed. About forty-five minutes later they came out. Mom looked terrible with dark circles around her eyes and tear stains on her dress.

"Uncle Mike and I are going out for dinner, and I want you all in bed by the time we get back," Mom demanded. That was their last dinner out. Uncle Mike left the following Sunday and died a few months later.

For days, Fu, Kati and I got the silent treatment. The following week Mom came into my room, gathered up all the clothes Dr. Grander had given me, and headed for the dump. On her return, she picked up the phone book and started dialing numbers. That's how she found my Yellow Page shrink.

"Mikala, from now on things are going to change. I will drive you to and from work."

"You will not see Shari again. Nor will you be signing up for any more of Dr. Grander's classes, or going to her for therapy. She will no longer be part of your life."

"I'll find a new therapist for you. It's either that, or it's time for you to move out. The choice is yours." Mom said sternly.

"What choice? I had nowhere to go! I've never had a choice about anything," I mumbled as I walked out of the room.

CHAPTER 18
YELLOW PAGE SHRINK

The following Monday, I reluctantly followed Mom into my new therapist's office. There he was, a bald, middle-aged, man sitting behind the cleanest desk I had ever seen. He reminded me of an owl with Harry Potter glasses. His professional but casual attire gave the impression of someone trying a little too hard to come across as anything but a shrink.

I looked at Mom. "Mom, No, we agreed I'd only go to female therapists!"

"Things have changed, Mikala. Dr. Manning will be your new therapist."

Dr. Manning looked past Mom and directly at me. "I'm sorry to hear I wasn't your choice. Mikala, How would you feel about having a few sessions before you form an opinion."

I crossed my arms, prepared to argue but decided it wasn't worth the effort. "I don't think I have a choice," I said.

An odd look crossed his face. "I wouldn't expect you to make up your mind until we've gotten to get to know each other. But it is fair to tell you I have ground rules for sessions and only treat patients who choose to work with me. Should we give it a little time?"

I looked at him and begrudgingly nodded.

"Would you start by telling me why you're here?" He looked at me as if he really expected a reply. I remained silent.

But, of course, Mom didn't. She quickly broke the silence. I couldn't help but smile as I listened to her version of Dr. Grander. *Well, she's right on, but he's probably not looking forward to treating a patient with a mom like her.*

"I understand you're frustrated, but I'd really like to hear from Mikala." The doctor looked at me, and again, I said nothing. With crossed arms and a cold stare, I ignored him. In response, he made no attempt to break our growing tension. After what seemed like forever, Mom broke the silence again.

"Mikala, Please!" Mom said.

I remained silent.

"After I fired Dr. Grander, I looked in the phone book, and you were the first therapist to call back," Mom continued.

For the first time, I saw the hint of a smile cross Dr. Manning's face. "Why don't you wait in the waiting room and let me talk to Mikala alone for a few minutes."

Oh great a Yellow Page shrink who thinks Mom will listen. I might as well make myself comfortable. I slumped further down in my chair. Mom looked as if she were going to cry, but quickly stood up and left the room. I was too angry to care.

Dr. Manning sat there watching me. My hands automatically began to straighten my wrinkled shirt. Finally, I couldn't stand the silence anymore and had to break it.

"What do you mean by ground rules, anyway?"

"I mean if you decide to be my patient, and if I agree to treat you, there are certain things we will have to agree upon."

"Like what?"

"Like treating each other with respect. That means being on time for appointments, being committed to our goals and being engaged in your therapy. Mikala, I'd like to help you, but to be honest, I have enough patients who need and want my help. I don't want to take on patients who won't put in the effort. So, you wouldn't be able to sit here and say nothing."

"Does Mom have to come with me?"

"No. You would be my patient and you'd decide what you want to share. All our therapy sessions will be confidential. That's not only a promise but protected by law."

"Some patients do find a team approach works best for them. They want their medical doctor, therapist and family to work together."

"Not ready for that," I responded.

"My question is, are you ready to start therapy at all?"

Desperate to leave, I nodded slightly.

"I'll take that as a yes?"

I nodded again.

Dr. Manning stood up and smiled at me. "Let's tell your Mom to set up another appointment. She's your driver, right?"

I smiled as I thought of that as Mom's role. *Driver? Yeah, she can be that.*

The Sunny Side of Crazy

CHAPTER 19
PRIVATE SESSIONS

Over the next few sessions, I participated just enough to remain Dr. Manning's patient. But by the seventh or eighth session, I found myself reluctantly looking forward to the next. Dr. Manning didn't pry or pressure, and as promised, he kept conversations between us. Unlike Dr. Grander, he refused to go down the "Mom won't let me grow up" path even when I tried.

"Mikala, you can't change other people, so let's focus on you." The more we'd talk, the more I would see I had some control after all.

Time passed quickly, and I found myself wanting to talk about my secret friends. Three months into therapy, I brought them up.

"Dr. Manning, I keep secret journals."

"Would you like to tell me about them?"

"No, but maybe I could let you read one."

"Do you write in your journal a lot?"

"Yeah, all the time. I have lots of them. Journals are Mom's go-to gifts for every occasion."

" Sometimes secrets are hard to talk about. Yes, I'd like to read one."

I sat quietly for what seemed like a long time. Finally, I asked him, "Have you ever had a patient with secret friends?"

"As a matter of fact, I have."

I wanted to ask if he thought they were crazy, but I was afraid.

"You know, Dr. Manning, I used to be someone else. I used to be a girl named Michiko, and I lived in Japan before I was adopted. I've been Mikala for a long time.

"Would you like to tell me what it was like to be Michiko?'

"No, not really. I don't remember her very well." But sometimes, I feel like I'm not Mikala either."

I stopped, expecting another question, but instead the doctor and I sat together as if lost in our own thoughts for a long time. The sound of his tapping pencil brought me back, and I left wondering if I'd said too much. Would I really have the courage to let him read my journals?

The next session I put one down on the edge of his desk.

He smiled, reached for the journal, opened it and read a few entries. Then he gently closed it and smiled at me.

"If you don't mind, I would like to read more and return it to you next week."

"Dr. Manning, I have secret friends who write to me and to each other in my journals."

"Would you like to tell me a little more about them, Mikala?"

I sat there a long time before I could begin. Finally, I said, "They have names. Their names are in the journal but some of the writing is pretty messy. Not all of them are left-handed like

I am. Sometimes they talk to me; I mean in my head. Maybe it sounds silly, but I know them and they know me really well! I guess you should know that before you start reading."

"You said their names are in the journal. How many secret friends write in your journals?"

" Five."

"Mikala, do you think it would be possible for me to talk to one of your friends?"

"Do you mean talk to them like you're talking to me?"

Dr. Manning smiled and nodded his head.

"I'm not sure, maybe. If so it would probably be Skye. I think she'd be the only one."

"Why is that?"

"Because she's the only one who thinks you know what you are doing!"

Dr. Manning's smile spread across his owlish face.

A week later Dr. Manning looked up to see Mikala as he hadn't seen her before. From what he'd read in her journal, and what she had said in the last session, the person entering his office was, no doubt, her secret friend, Skye.

"Hello, Dr. Manning. I'm Skye. May I sit down?"

"Of course, please do," Dr. Manning replied, as he quickly jotted notes in the file in front of him — Skye appears confident, mature, makes direct eye contact, is relaxed.

"I'm glad you're here, Skye. I've read your entries in--"

145

"I know," Skye replied before he could finish. " I know," Skye replied again as she leaned back in her chair. Once comfortable, she crossed her legs and smoothed her hair. Skye was dressed in a flattering white v-neck sweater with neatly creased black slacks. The sunlight reflected off her crystal earrings. It was easy to imagine Skye as the sophisticated and sexy friend in Mikala's journal. She was a dramatic contrast to ultra-casual Mikala.

It seemed like Skye had every intention of controlling the session. Dr. Manning leaned back and decided to let her take the lead.

"Well, I'm here Dr. Manning. Do you have questions?"

In his mind, Dr. Manning quickly began to prioritize his questions. He needn't have bothered. Skye went on talking.

"If I were you, I'd want to know everything about me and my relationship with Miki, but I hardly think that's possible. It's so complicated. I'll tell you what I can." The authority in her voice was unmistakable. So, as much as Dr. Manning disliked the phrase, "If I were you," he let it pass. Time was short, and he wanted to hear everything Skye had to say.

"Yes, I'd like to know as much as you can tell me about Mikala."

"Well, you know she's different!"

"I've gotten to know Mikala pretty well, but I don't remember her saying she's different."

"Oh, she knows. She's known for a long time, but she keeps her secrets."

146

The Sunny Side of Crazy

"And what secrets would those be?"

"Us, her secret friends. She doesn't talk about us. She hides us in her journals. But then, she gave you one, didn't she? Now, here I am. That's different, isn't it doctor? I mean she knows something's wrong but not what or why."

"And, how about you, Skye, do you know what's wrong and why?"

"Isn't that your job? Isn't that why she is seeing you, Dr. Manning?"

Dr. Manning was a bit surprised by how cleverly Skye avoided answering.

"Miki's mother brought her here because she's worried. She's a bit overprotective, you know. She's afraid to let Miki grow up. But, I'm helping. I mean as sweet as Miki is, she's not the sharpest knife in the drawer."

Dr. Manning smiled as he scribbled more notes. Skye showed a sense of humor that was lacking in Mikala. She talked non-stop, telling him about how well she did things, her many talents and how much Mikala depended on her.

On and on, she went. By the time she'd finished talking about herself, Dr. Manning was both intrigued and frustrated. He wanted to hear more about her relationship with Mikala but heard his next patient pacing back and forth in the waiting room. There was only enough time for one more question.

"Where has Mikala been while we've been talking?"

"Oh, she's here," Skye answered, pointing to her head. "But I doubt she'll remember anything. She forgets a lot, you know."

"Skye. I'd really like to talk more, but I have another patient waiting."

"Oh, of course," Skye replied, as she gracefully stood up and left the room.

Dr. Manning watched her leave, sat down and jotted down a few more notes before inviting his next patient in.

CHAPTER 20
DIAGNOSIS

As I sat in his office, Dr. Manning's words remained frozen in the air between us. They were cold, impersonal words. They sounded frightening, raw and sterile. I shivered as his diagnosis cut through my light summer T-shirt and into my thin, fragile bones.

"Dissociative Identity Disorder formerly referred to as Multiple Personalities," he said.

Dissociative Identity Disorder, Multiple Personality? A condition? A diagnosis? I sat motionless as his words sunk in.

At first, they made no sense. They tumbled through my mind so quickly. I could barely comprehend them. Then, slowly, they settled into a pattern, an explanation I didn't want to hear. Thoughts started spiraling, and questions reverberated around in my brain, my body tensed as I stared at the dying ivy on Dr. Manning's immaculate desk.

How strange, I thought. *Isn't this supposed to be a place of health, hope and new beginnings?*

The bald doctor sat motionless behind his desk. His wire-rimmed glasses were perched on his hawkish nose, and his hands were folded gently across his pot belly, as if in prayer. I briefly wondered if he was the same therapist I'd been seeing for months.

"You need to water your plant, Doctor."

It seemed like forever before he spoke again. This time his voice was familiar. It was filled with compassion and warmth.

"Mikala, How do you feel? Are you okay?"

"How do I feel? I don't know how to feel." I slowly repeated his words. "Multiple   Personalities?"

"Dissociative Identity Disorder would be the diagnosis," he corrected me.

"Are you kidding me? In other words, I really am crazy?"

"Is that what you heard me say, Mikala?" he continued.

"The same thing isn't it?

"No, not at all! You created alter personalities for a reason. Dissociative Identity Disorder is a very creative way some children use to survive trauma. It explains your periods of lost time, severe anxiety and many of your other symptoms. Some of the same symptoms exist in other disorders, but I've read your journals and talked to one of your secret friends. I'm confident Dissociative Identity Disorder is the correct diagnosis."

"If that's true, why didn't my other therapists tell me?"

"Well, as I said, many of your symptoms are found in other disorders, and to be perfectly honest, some therapists don't believe Dissociative Identity Disorder exists. I do. You're not my first patient suffering from this disorder, and I've had experience treating it."

I stared at the bookcases lining the wall behind the doctor. *So, is this what it meant? Sam, Mom's little helper, Calle the*

*clown, and Suki the aspiring teacher were just different pieces
of me? Were they just parts of one deranged mind? Mine? What
about talented Skye, who wanted to grow up to be a singer? Oh,
and, of course, nasty Tin who tried to hide anger but exploded
at a moment's notice? I wondered why I'd shown Dr. Manning
my journals and let him speak to Skye.*

Of course, I'd wanted an explanation for my craziness, but
this? No thanks, it was just too bizarre! *My God, multiple
personalities? Weren't people with multiple personalities the
serial killers, predators, and demonically possessed that movies
were made about! This was no movie, It was my life!*

Still, I knew Dr. Manning was right. It made perfect sense.
It explained my secret companions, my memory lapses and
being blamed for things I didn't believe I'd done. How could I
not have known? I was hearing the truth, and every cell in my
body knew it.

"Mikala, I know this is a lot to take in, but I want you to
understand, you're not alone. As I said before, I've treated
patients with Dissociative Identity Disorder. I've helped them,
and I can help you."

"Did you cure them?" I could no longer hold back my tears,
and for the first time in ages, I cried.

"I'm not sure cured is the right word." Dr. Manning replied
as he handed me a box of tissues from the edge of his desk "But,
now that we have a diagnosis, if you choose, we can proceed
with a treatment plan."

"What kind of treatment plan?" I'd already spent more
than twenty years living with secrets and behaviors I didn't

understand. Of course, I wanted a treatment plan. I wanted to live without "secret companions" fucking up my life, leaving me to take the blame and clean up their messes. I dried my eyes, silenced my sniffles, and said, "Dr. Manning, I'm so tired of being punished for things I didn't do, and not doing things I should have done. I don't want to live this way anymore!"

"I just want to be a normal person, I just want to be me!"

"Mikala, do you think your alters might be controlling you?

I didn't respond.

Dr. Manning took a deep breath and watched me, as if he wanted to say something more but held back. This was followed by a long silence. Perhaps my history of self-destructive behavior had crossed his mind as quickly as it crossed mine.

Finally, "I understand Mikala, I really do. And, you need to understand that you have options. Some patients with Dissociative Identity Disorder decide to integrate their alters and others decide to focus on managing them better. I had one patient who decided she didn't want to change anything. She simply wanted a diagnosis, an explanation for why she did the things she did. Your treatment plan has to be your decision."

"You shouldn't decide right this moment. You need to take time to think about it. But Mikala, remember you have to make the decision, not me, and not your mother. You're the one who will do the work, go through the process and live with the results."

Dr. Manning stopped, scratched his head, leaned forward in his chair, and softened his voice further, "If you choose to integrate, any childhood trauma that you've repressed will have to be brought from your subconscious to your conscious where we can process it. It's not painful in a physical sense, but emotionally, it can be disturbing."

Disturbing? Living in a world of craziness, that's what's disturbing!

Dr. Manning paused, waiting for a sign that I understood.

I nodded slightly.

"If you choose to integrate your personalities, I will hypnotize you. Do you understand what that means?"

"Of course! It sounds weird. I mean none of my other therapists suggested it."

"That doesn't surprise me. Not all therapists consider it valid. I do. I've been well trained and successful using it."

I was no longer listening but lost in my own thoughts. *What would it be like to live like everyone else, to have control over my thoughts and behaviors? The possibility began to excite me and was followed by a feeling I didn't recognize. What was it? Could it be hope? What if this doctor finally had the answer? What if his process worked, and what if I could be normal? I let myself feel it; I let myself feel hope!*

"Mikala, how would you feel about scheduling your next appointment for Monday. You can think about things over the weekend, and then we can talk some more. This is an important decision, and as I said, it's one only you can make. It shouldn't be made lightly or quickly"

I nodded in agreement. I knew he was right. Mom would have an opinion, a strong one, she always did. And, when Mom started, she didn't know when to stop. I needed quiet. I needed time to think.

I wondered if my lifelong secret friends would have to die. "So, Dr. Manning, what would happen to them, the others? I mean, what if I needed…"

Dr. Manning didn't wait for me to finish. He smiled. "They would become aspects of your own personality. You would be a young lady in control of your own life."

"Dr. Manning, if I'm hypnotized, could Mom be with me?"

He looked pleasantly surprised, smiled and nodded. "If you'd like."

The doctor watched me for a moment and slowly began tapping his pen on his desk, a subtle but sure sign the session was over. I glanced at the small clock sitting on top of his filing cabinet. It was already after four, exactly eleven minutes past my 50-minute allotment. I stood up, grabbed my backpack, forced a smile, and said, "Okay Doc, see you Monday."

I left Dr. Manning's office filled with hope. Hope that I could be normal. *That's what I wanted, wasn't it? At least I was sure it was before I knew it was a possibility.* I struggled against the urge to run to Mom for hugs, comfort and encouraging words. How many times had I heard her say, "Don't worry, Mikala, everything will be okay? It wasn't always true. Things didn't always turn out okay. In fact, sometimes they got worse, and I couldn't let that happen this time.

CHAPTER 21

SANCTUARY

Outside, Mom with her windblown blond hair, was waiting in her beloved convertible, top-down and radio playing. She closed her book and glanced up with her eyes mostly hidden behind the oversized sunglasses she wore rain or shine. Before starting the car, she smiled at me and asked her usual annoying, post-session question.

"How did it go, Honey?"

She was always curious about my sessions, and today was no different.

"Fine," I lied. A little different I guess."

I wanted reassurance, I needed to hear Mom say, "Everything will be okay, Miki." But today had to be different. I needed to stay in control.

"What was different about today's session?"

Catching myself, I looked away and struggled not to engage. Then, I looked at her and wondered why she hadn't figured it out. *Why didn't she know what was wrong with me? After all, how many times had she accused me of doing things I had not done? Blamed me? Punished me? Why didn't she believe me when I told her the truth, when I said, I don't remember, or I did not do it?*

I felt my anger rise and quickly looked away. Today, for sure, I could do without questions and false reassurances. So it was with a great deal of relief I heard her say, "I hope you don't mind if we skip McDonald's and go straight home. I've got errands to run.

I used to think Mom's errands meant going on a dinner date or maybe even a brief affair, but her numerous TJ Maxx, Marshalls and HomeGoods shopping bags attested to the fact she preferred shopping to dating. Either way, I'd have a couple of hours alone. Perfect!

"Go ahead, Mom, I don't mind." As soon as the words were out of my mouth, I knew it wasn't entirely true. I wanted to go back in time, to a time when we talked for hours, a time when I believed what she said and thought I could depend on her. But I was younger then. Now, I knew it wouldn't happen. Those days were long gone. Recent conversations were few and far between, quickly turning into arguments, which neither of us ever won. I continued to stare out the window.

Mom pulled into the driveway and followed me through the garage into the kitchen. The moment I opened the door, the silence was broken by our two cute, barking and extremely annoying dogs. They raced around, yapping, dancing in circles and breaking my train of thought.

I love our kitchen. It's a warm, cheerful room where the sun streams in through an oversized bay window.

It's the perfect environment for conversation and nourishment. Bright drawings and photos cover every inch of our refrigerator with one large overstuffed cookie jar on the counter next to it.

The Sunny Side of Crazy

The room was originally designed for a serious, accomplished chef. It contained at least one of every cooking device imaginable, as well as a large array of barely-read cookbooks. The state-of-the-art kitchen gives the mistaken impression that a cook might live here.

Not so, I thought. I smiled at the shiny bread machine sitting next to the Crock-pot. I was still waiting for the touch, taste and smell of the warm, crusty, fresh bread Mom promised to make. I doubted I would ever see it. It's just not Mom!

Several plaques hung above the pantry, identifying the true purpose of the room. It's the peace zone, the source of three-ingredient meals and of course, the drug chocolate. I stared at the signs.

Chocolate doesn't ask silly questions, Chocolate understands.

Chocolate comes from cocoa, a tree, therefore it's a plant, therefore chocolate is a salad.

No sense in being pessimistic, wouldn't work anyway.

In addition, the colorful tile hanging over the stove said it all, "Domestically Challenged!" *Funny,* I thought, *the picture on it bears a striking resemblance to Mom!*

"Honey, take the dogs out while I fix their dinner."

"Okay."

I watched her for a moment. Strange, I thought, *Mom could usually read me so well. But, today I got life-changing news, and she hasn't noticed. Mom is a smart, well-educated woman, she really should have noticed.* I didn't want to talk but I needed to, and meanwhile, Mom was totally engaged in selecting dog food flavors. *Good going Mom, just great!*

"Miki, I left your dinner in the fridge."

Dinner? Really? Only Mom could refer to cold, sticky spaghetti as dinner. Being a good cook wasn't a priority. Her idea of a home-cooked meal was Stouffers.

I took the dogs out, returned, leaned against the counter and watched Mom, still deciding on the dog's "din-din" from a choice of prime, gourmet meals. She prepared it as if it were the most important meal of the day, and to be truthful, it looked a whole lot better than the pile of cold spaghetti waiting for me.

"I have to pick the girls up and-----"

"Take your time Mom, take your time."

As her car pulled out of the driveway, I wondered why I felt so angry. I felt abandoned, but hadn't I been the one to blow her off whenever she tried to talk? Wasn't I the one who said, "Go ahead Mom, I don't mind?" And, wasn't I the one pretending everything was just fine?

Why was I so reluctant to ask for help? I wanted to know what she thought. Was it pride or was I afraid she wouldn't be willing to go through yet another crisis with me? She'd always been there when I needed her. She was a forever mother in every sense. But lately, things have been rocky. I wondered if she would stand by me if I chose integration, and if not, would I have the courage to go through it alone? Too tired to think, I left the kitchen and made my way down the long hallway to my bedroom.

The Sunny Side of Crazy

Rambo and Rebel, sedated from their evening meal, followed closely behind my plate of cold spaghetti.

My bedroom is beautiful. A huge window lets the sun stream in almost every morning. It's pretty in a childish way. The off-white walls, beige bedspread and soft pink pillows were Mom's choice, but everything else, including the hundreds of Beanie Babies and My Little Ponies that line the bookshelves, well, they're mine! Even at my age, I remember the name of each Beanie Baby, as well as the date I got it. Shari said it was silly for someone my age to keep such collections. So what? They make me happy.

The Mikala other people know is different in ways they can't possibly understand. They find me confusing because I can complete complicated puzzles in record time, draw detailed maps, or remember important and unimportant details. But, I can't always remember what I did the day before.

I felt tears welling up, as I looked at the beautiful 2,500 piece puzzle, my masterpiece, hanging above my bed. Beautifully framed in an elaborate silver frame it shows a magnificent, multi-colored monarch with clusters of smaller butterflies in the background. That butterfly symbolizes everything I want to be— beautiful and free.

In a moment of insight, it hit me. I'm just a big, incomplete puzzle. A beautiful butterfly with separate pieces. If Dr. Manning is right, I can put them together. That would be integration, wouldn't it?

I glanced at the antique trunk sitting at the end of my bed. I'd never liked that chest. Mom had stenciled "Miki's Hope Chest" on the front, and underneath I'd painted "The trunk."

Next to those words, I had drawn a baby elephant with the longest trunk you've ever seen.

Mom told me it was a hope chest for my future. I always thought of it as holding clutter from the past. I didn't know what hope was back then.

But, I knew elephants, and they were supposed to have great memories. Maybe, this chest could help me find mine. I slid down next to the trunk and propped it open. It was stuffed with photos, artwork, report cards, envelopes and other memorabilia. *Where do I start? In the beginning. First things first,* I thought. I pulled out a large manila envelope and emptied the contents on the floor. A little red passport with the picture of the saddest little girl I've ever seen fell out. It was me. Next to it, a small envelope with the return address of a Dr. Takagi. It was empty.

Then, I pulled out the Mickey Mouse bag lying on top. As soon as I set it beside me, a flood of memories came over me.

I felt overwhelming sadness as my mind drifted back to that dreary, rainy day in Japan so many years ago. *I wondered at the indifference with which my birth mother gave me away. Was it painful? Yes! Traumatic? Yes! Repressed? No. I remembered it as if it were yesterday. Was that what broke me into pieces? Or was it my foreign life with its endless challenges?*

The sound of a car pulling back into the driveway followed by two short beeps announced Mom's arrival home. I quickly tossed White Rabbit on my bed. "You're sleeping with me tonight." A couple of minutes later Mom was knocking on my door.

The Sunny Side of Crazy

"Are you okay, Miki?"

"Yeah, I'm just organizing my room"

"Well okay, but it's getting late, Honey."

"I know, I'm going to bed now."

"Okay then, I'll see you in the morning."

"Yeah, see you in the morning, Mom."

I waited, listening for her to leave. Instead, I heard her say in a very small voice, "I love you, baby girl. "Fresh tears rolled down my cheeks, I crawled in bed, exhausted, but relieved knowing Mom would be there for me, just as she'd always been.

The Sunny Side of Crazy

CHAPTER 22
DO NOT DISTURB

It was almost nine o'clock on Saturday morning when I woke up to a loud pounding on my door. It was Mom.

"Miki, it's 9 o'clock. You're late. Come on. You're gonna get fired!"

"I'm not going, Mom."

"What do you mean you're not going?"

"I'm sick."

Mom remained quiet for a whole thirty seconds.

"What do you mean you're sick? Open the door!"

I knew she wouldn't go away until I did, so I reluctantly stumbled my way to the door and cracked it open. Mom was standing outside the door in her weekend outfit: faded blue jeans; a white blouse; gym shoes; and sunglasses. She reached out to feel my head. I ducked and made my way back to my bed.

"Mom, go away. I have a bad headache. Let me sleep. I've already called in."

It was rare for me to miss work. If there was one thing I was known for, it was dependability. My bosses didn't know what to make of me. I tried their patience daily, but I was always there and exactly on time.

"Are you sure you're okay, Miki ?"

The Sunny Side of Crazy

"Yeah, Mom, I'm fine."

"Well, all right then, I have to take your sisters to the theater. Do you need anything? "No, Mom!"

Just a little peace and quiet, I thought as I heard Mom's car pull out of the driveway. I slipped on my old black sweats and a clean T-shirt. After brushing my teeth, I pulled my hair back into a sloppy ponytail and headed for the kitchen. I hadn't eaten anything since last night's cold spaghetti and I was starving. But, I was even more eager to get back to my trunk. I settled on a cream cheese bagel and a glass of chocolate milk, which I carefully carried back to my room and set down next to the trunk.

Finally, I could think. I needed to decide if I should tell Mom about yesterday's session. It had been a long time since we'd talked about anything, not that she didn't try. I would become argumentative and defensive, then finally agree with Mom, and do just the opposite. Mom said I was passive-aggressive, but I was just trying to get her off my back. On the other hand, Mom always thought she was right, and sometimes, she wasn't!

I knew my trunk contained more information, clues and critical pieces to my hidden trauma so I opened it. Sticking out was another large manila envelope. I dumped the old photos on the floor.

My thoughts turned to my earliest days in America.

When I first arrived, I didn't feel anything for my new mother, other than annoyance. She wanted to be close to me, and that made me angry. I just wanted to be left alone, and she wouldn't let me. It seemed like she was always in my face. And what was worse, she lied about important things right from the start.

Over and over, she said, "Shimpai shi nai de" (Don't worry) and "Dai joubu" (it will be okay). But it wasn't true then, and it still isn't.

I spent the next couple of hours looking at old report cards, first-place ribbons and newspaper articles about some of my other childhood accomplishments.

Memories can be exhausting. I decided to take a break. I must have slept for hours because I awoke to the sound of laughter and the smell of hot pepperoni pizza. I hadn't eaten since my morning bagel, and I was feeling hungry again.

My little sister Fu, always returned from her auditions with a great deal of fanfare, a huge appetite and lots of belly laughs that resonated throughout the house. Smells of the pizza and happy sounds of laughter told me she got a part in the play and was now playing cook in the kitchen. Her talent was acting, not cooking, and I was sure that the pizza arrived in a cardboard box. Kim's real contribution was limited to heating garlic bread, putting pickles on top of the pizza and handing out paper plates. No matter, I needed food, so I shook out my crampy legs and limped into the kitchen.

Kim grinned as she told me she had a role in the Main Street performance of "Annie."

"Did you get the part you wanted?"

"Uh no, but I got a smaller part. I play one of the little orphans left behind. So sad, but so appropriate. Don't you think?"

As a talented actress, Kim's ability to stay positive in the face of rejection amazed me.

"The main role probably went to the director's daughter again, didn't it? You're a great actress Kim, and you deserve bigger parts."

"Yeah, it did, and I know I do, but I guess people just aren't ready for a Chinese Annie."

I tried to grab a paper plate out of her hand as I opened the lid of the pizza box. Kim held on tightly.

"I'm sorry, Miki. Mom said you weren't feeling well so I only ordered enough for us," Kim giggled, as she pushed me aside and grabbed the largest slice from the box.

I picked up another plate, sat down at the table and watched Kim. Despite the cheese dribbling down her chin and an outfit designed for what she was yet to become, she was just as cute as the day she arrived. I felt annoyed and had a tinge of jealousy,

"Don't you get tired of being passed over for bigger roles?" I asked.

Her attempted answer never found its way past the cheese and sausage. Two slices later, I was ready to head back to my room.

"Hey Kim, want to see what I found in my trunk?"

The Sunny Side of Crazy

"Nope, I'm gonna play on the computer. Miki, why don't you play with me. You've never played. Come on. You'll like it. Guaranteed. Come see! "

"It's not real. It's just a silly computer game."

"I know it's not real but you can create all these neat things."

My explosive response took me by surprise; I was angry and quickly snapped back,

"For God's sake, Kim, I said I don't want to play. It's a stupid game. You've told me about it, and I DO NOT WANT TO PLAY!"

"Okay, Okay, Okay, you don't have to be so touchy ."she replied.

"It's a stupid game, Kim. it's not real. Everything is on the computer, not real, just in your head."

Kim gave me one of her familiar "what the heck is wrong with you" looks and turned away.

The words I'd just spoken, "not real and just in your head" echoed in my mind. I felt sick. I made a dash for the bathroom. By the time I returned Kim was gone, and Mom was sitting there waiting for me. She pointed toward the patio. I picked up a Coke and followed her outside.

I followed to the lounge chairs placed side by side under a huge red umbrella and set my Coke down on one of the little tables. A cool breeze carried the peaceful smell of jasmine across our yard, making it the most unlikely setting for the confrontation to follow.

Angry thoughts flooded through my mind. *Mom should have known my diagnosis! I shouldn't have had to wait for a damn therapist to diagnose me. She knew something was wrong. She was with me every single day for years. Didn't she care? Didn't she give a shit?*

"Miki, what's going on?" Mom asked.

"Dr. Manning gave me a new label today. He said I have Dissociative Identity Disorder. It used to be called Multiple Personalities."

Silence!

I was annoyed by her lack of response. She usually had so much to say. What was she thinking? Finally, a small nod of acknowledgment. Now, I needed to hear her say something, anything. But she just sat there looking at me.

"Mom, stop! You are looking at me like I'm from outer space. Did you hear what I said? Dr. Manning diagnosed me with Multiple Personalities, like the psychos in movies."

Mom continued to stare at me as if she were struggling to comprehend.

"Mom!"

"I heard you, Miki, I'm just not sure what that means. Do you think he's right?"

My anger came bubbling to the surface.

"Well, I guess. After all, you chose him, didn't you? So he's gotta be right," I answered in a sarcastic voice.

The Sunny Side of Crazy

I watched Mom's face turn red. She took a deep breath and chose her words carefully. Slowly and clearly, she asked, "Miki, what did Dr. Manning say?"

"He said, I was a very creative child who split into pieces to survive childhood trauma and I have repressed memories that need to be brought to the surface. If I do that, I will be able to process the trauma and be good to go. Oh, and he doesn't like the name, multiple personalities. He says it's called Dissociative Identity Disorder. But, that's just another label, another diagnosis, one more way of saying, I'm crazy."

Mom sat perfectly still and stared at me.

In a sarcastic tone, I continued, "He said I have a choice. I can continue as I am and learn to control my personalities, or I can integrate them."

Mom's expression told me our conversation was doomed unless I changed my tone. I couldn't help myself. I had to put my anger somewhere. It sizzled and flared again as more harsh words flew out of my mouth.

"Yeah, I think he's right! Good God, Mom, I think you should have known. I can't believe you didn't. You should have. You're my mother!" I screamed.

Mom sat there staring at me, remaining uncharacteristically quiet. I took a deep breath and started in again.

"Mom, you blamed me for so many things I didn't do. Don't you remember how many times you accused me of lying? You said there could only be one truth. Well, guess what Mom? In my case, that wasn't true. I was accused, blamed and punished for so many things I didn't do."

The Sunny Side of Crazy

Expecting Mom to meet my anger with her own, I was unprepared for her reaction. Instead of denial, justification, or anger, in a very low voice, barely above a whisper, she asked,

"What's it like Miki? Tell me what it's like to have Dissociative Identity Disorder?"

I'd spent all morning remembering the past and feeding my anger. I hadn't thought about what it felt like. How could I explain something I didn't understand? How could I possibly describe my normal?

"Mom, do you remember taking me into a fun house at the carnival when I was about eight? I didn't want to go in but you insisted. You said the same thing you always said, don't worry Miki, it'll be okay."

"Fun? I hated it! All those distorted images terrified me. I was caught in all those versions of myself, and I didn't know which one was me. Maybe they all were. Maybe they all are! Each one living a life of their own, doing as they please. They do things I wouldn't. I don't always know what I've done or why? And, I NEVER knew why you were so angry at me.

It's hard to explain. I know them, I love them, and I need them. They've been my best friends for as long as I can remember. They've taken care of me. Sometimes better than anyone else, even you!"

We sat looking at each other. Mom was speechless. I was drained and afraid I'd gone too far. Mom looked old, sad and exhausted. I thought she was going to cry. There was so much more I wanted to say, but all the anger had been sucked out of me. Our beautiful summer afternoon had turned cold.

The Sunny Side of Crazy

"Mom, I'm tired. Can we talk in the morning?"

She nodded and slowly rose out of her chair.

"Mom, Dr. Manning said something else. He said I have a decision to make. I need to decide if I want to stay like I am and learn to control my personalites, or integrate them into my own personality. And, he said I need to decide by myself. I repeated I NEED TO DECIDE WHAT TO DO BY MYSELF. I HAVE TO MAKE THIS DECISION ON MY OWN!"

"Miki, that's fine. But are you going to let them live your life for you? For the first time, if you have a chance ..."

"MOM, STOP! " I interrupted.

"I'm sorry, you're right, Miki. You know I love you and just want the very best for you."

Mom leaned over for a quick good-night kiss, but I quickly turned away. I could see she was fighting tears as we went back into the house. We retreated to our separate rooms. Me, to my trunk, and Mom to her computer to google Dissociative Identity Disorder.

Back in my room, I slid down next to my trunk. Confused, frustrated and angry, I wondered why I was blaming Mom. I knew whatever decision I made, she would be there for me just like she'd always been. I reached down and picked up a small Hello Kitty photo album and flipped it open. A smiling baby looked back at me. Each page held one 3X5 photo of a happy, healthy bundle of joy looking directly into the camera. But the last one wasn't a baby. It was of a little girl about four years old. No longer smiling, it was of one sad little girl sitting alone in her nursery school.

I wondered if there were other pictures back in Japan. Where were the pictures of a sleeping baby in her mother's lap, or of a toddler with her adoring papa? Where were the pictures of the baby's first steps? I stared at the name. It looked unfamiliar. *How strange I didn't recognize my own name. My name was Michiko, like the Empress of Japan. My mother gave me a beautiful name and then gave me away. How weird! How could she do that?*

I felt no connection to that child, just curiosity. I was feeling the same way about myself.

Who in the heck is Mikala anyway?

CHAPTER 23
THROUGH A MOTHER'S EYES

I don't know how long I sat staring at the screen. Within five minutes of turning on my computer, there it was, a perfect description of Mikala's behavior. It had been right there the whole time I'd been desperately searching for an explanation.

I felt sick, angry. I shoved my chair back, flung myself on my bed. The disorder was a thief. It had stolen valuable time, and if not discovered, could have completely destroyed our relationship.

Wasn't it only a week ago that I told Mikala if she didn't change her behavior, she would have to move out? Guilt intertwined with my anger, and I let myself cry. When my sobs finally subsided, I was emotionally drained and a deep sadness overcame me. Mikala was right. I had blamed her for what she hadn't done, and there were consequences. Sometimes harsh ones. Mikala must have been as confused by my behavior as I was by hers.

"Mom, why didn't you buy chocolate ice cream ?" I remembered.

"Because you said Strawberry was your favorite, " I had told her.

" I never said that."

"Sure you did, don't you remember?"

"I never said that." she had remarked.

"Sure, don't you remember?" I urged her.

"I never said that." she insisted.

"Mom, why did you buy Kim a pretty coat and me an ugly one?" she asked.

"What? You chose it, Miki." I had frustratingly replied.

"No, I didn't. You always buy her cute clothes." she said begrudgingly.

"Miki, you got an A in this last semester. Why a D now?" I had demanded.

" I don't know. I tried," She meagerly answered.

"Obviously not hard enough!" I had replied.

There were so many clues, and I had overlooked them all. Sometimes, she wrote with her right hand, sometimes her left. I thought having imaginary friends during childhood was normal. I rationalized everything. But what about the occasional duck walk?

"Miki, straighten your feet. You're walking like a duck." I had warned.

"Mom, I'm not!" she insisted.

It was probably the result of her broken leg. But why sometimes? Well, she's probably just tired. So much seemed so odd, but I never thought of it as a symptom. Was I just being naive?

Now, it all made sense. I wanted to talk to Mikala. To tell her I was sorry that I didn't understand. I made my way to

Mikala's room and knocked on her door. She ignored me. I returned to my room. It took a few days for me to see her diagnosis as the miracle it was meant to be!

The Sunny Side of Crazy

CHAPTER 24
A SISTER'S WISDOM

I glanced out the window. What a surprise. It was pitch dark. Had I really been lost in memories all afternoon? I laid down and watched the overhead fan circle above me. The slight breeze felt good, and in a way, so did I. I was surrounded by memories, and most were good! Class photos, prom photos, Mary Kate and Ashley magazines and Disney badges. There were pictures of my sisters and me laughing at the beach and belly dancing in the kitchen.

Now I had a diagnosis, and the pieces of my puzzle were falling into place.

I was wondering where to look for the last few pieces when Kim burst into my room with her rendition of "wake up sleepy head, it's almost time for bed."

She stopped abruptly and looked around my room.

"God, Miki, what happened here?" she wondered out loud.

I didn't answer.

"Mom wants you to come out for dinner."

Turning on her heels, she raced back to the kitchen to share the news of my messy room with mom. Parts of me were scattered all around the room. *Well, my room was messy but my mind was beginning to clear.*

I made my way to the kitchen where Mom and I pretended our confrontation had never happened. We were abnormally nice to each other.

" Miki, can I get you more of…?"

"No, it's okay. Do you want me to help clean…?"

"I can do it," offered Kim

Even Kati joined in. "I'll take the dogs out," she said.

I knew Mom had told my sisters about my diagnosis. It wasn't normal for them to be so helpful. So, that's why the house had been so quiet.

"Thanks, guys." I mumbled as I headed back to my room. I stepped over the mess, crawled into bed and slept until a little after midnight. Waking up, I was overcome by a desire to talk. I wanted to talk. Actually I needed to talk.

I tiptoed to Kim's door and peeked in. She was sprawled sideways across her bed snoring. Despite finding Kim annoying, I've always loved her. Looking at her, I realized she wasn't a little girl anymore. Slowly, I pushed Kim's door open.

"Hey, Kim!"

Silence.

"Kim, are you awake," I whispered.

No response.

I don't know how long I stood there hoping she would reply.

Increasing my volume, "Are you awake, Kim ?"

The Sunny Side of Crazy

" I wasn't, but I am now. What do you want, Miki?"

"I need to talk," I said.

"Now? Are you kidding? It's after midnight!" she grumbled.

"I know, but just for a few minutes, and you can show me your computer game."

After a long pause, I heard, "Oh God, Miki, are you crazy? Oh okay, come on in." she groaned, stretching and stumbling her way to her desk where she switched on the light and computer.

With a stroke of her fingers both Kim and the computer sprang to life. Several digital versions of her danced across the screen. One morphed into another and another and then another. Different hairstyles, different outfits and different expressions, but they were all Kim.

"Kim, I thought you created different characters. They all look like you!

"They are me! Only they have different personalities and different lives. There're my avatars, you know, alters?"

"Wait, what? What did you say?" I was startled.

"I said, I control their lives. It's fun! Let's play."

I stared at Kim, "You call them alters!" I stammered.

"Yeah, sometimes. Usually, avatars, characters, or whatever. I can create some for you. if you want."

I felt sick! Kim kept talking but I didn't hear her words. I was going back and forth between her "I want to control their lives" and Dr. Manning's comment, "Maybe your alters are controlling your life."

"Kim, I need to tell you something. But you have to keep it between us" I pleaded.

"Shoot," she said casually not knowing the severity of what I was about to lay on her.

"Yesterday, Dr. Manning diagnosed me with Multiple Personalities. It means…"

She cut me off. "I know what it means! Like in the movie *Sybil,* right?"

I wondered how she could remember a movie I'd forgotten so long ago.

"Not exactly. I don't know. I just know what Dr. Manning said, and I don't want to believe it. I mean it makes me sound like I could be dangerous or something."

"He could be wrong," she said.

"No, he's right. I've been mislabeled before but not this time. I know he's right. It is like other people live inside me and do things I don't remember doing. I think it was an alter who cut off all your hair."

I handed her a picture from my trunk, and she burst into one of her famous belly laughs.

"Oh my gosh, Miki, I looked so cute. Just like a little Buddhist monk!"

" I more than cut your hair off, I nicked your scalp," I said with shame.

" Really? I don't remember that," she answered.

"Do you remember being pushed down the stairs?" I asked.

"Nope, I guess I was too young," she said.

"One of my alters, Tin, was so jealous of you. I think it was Tin who pushed you down the stairs. Maybe you don't remember because you were only two but Mom caught you just before you landed on the tile below. I could have killed you."

Kim looked confused.

"And Kim, what about the way I pushed you around the house?" I started.

I handed her another picture. In this one I was standing behind her, hands on her shoulders pushing her in the direction I wanted her to go. In the picture, she was smiling.

"Oh yeah," she laughed. "I remember playing choo choo with you. You were pushing me around all the time. Is that what you're talking about?" she asked.

"Yeah, I put my hands on your shoulders and made you go wherever I wanted you to," I admitted.

"I thought we were having fun!" she said.

"What I'm trying to say is, it wasn't me who did that!" I said.

"Whatever, Whoever!" Kim's replied quickly.

"Weren't you ever angry?" I implored.

The Sunny Side of Crazy

I was surprised. she only had fragments of these memories. She remembered little of the mean things I had done to her.

"Miki, I hardly remember those things. It was so long ago. Anyway, what do you think of Dr. Manning's diagnosis?" she asked.

"It's right on," I said.

"It makes sense, I guess," she said.

"What did you say, Kim?" I asked,

"I said it makes sense. I mean you know how moody and unpredictable you can be. Sometimes, you're happy and the next minute, you're pissed off about something. I've never known why. You know Miki, Mom and I have been walking on eggshells for a long, long time. You've been controlling us, too," she responded.

"What do you mean?" I asked.

"I mean things have revolved around you and your moods for as long as I can remember," she said.

I felt tears welling up in my eyes, and Kim quickly looked at her computer pretending not to notice.

"We love you anyway Miki. You know that, don't you?" she asked.

I nodded and changed the subject.

"Dr. Manning says I can continue to live as I am, or go through a process of integration. Then my alters would no longer control me, but I guess they would still be part of me.

Does that make sense?"I asked, wondering if it even made sense to me.

"I suppose; I don't know, Miki," she said.

"I think it would make me feel normal, don't you?" I asked almost as if asking myself.

Before she could answer, my stomach rumbled and growled so loudly we both started laughing.

"It's time!" she said.

"For pancakes," I finished.

In record time, we were in the kitchen, pulling milk from the fridge and pancake mix from the pantry. We were giddy, hungry and a bit too noisy. A single bark from Mom's room warned us. We immediately went silent and stood still. No dogs showed up, and better yet, no Mom. We tried to quiet each other but our stomach grumbles grew to a roar and our giggles turned to laughter. We couldn't help ourselves. Still, no one came.

Relieved, Kim mixed the batter, I got out plates and silverware, and together we hunted for the syrup. Soon we were sitting at the table looking at the most beautiful pancakes we'd ever seen. They weren't round and maybe a bit dark around the edges, but they were, by far, the best pancakes we'd ever had.

After filling our stomachs, we began to feel the effects of the long night. It was almost four in the morning and there was no way we could clean up our mess. Agreeing that it would be waiting in the morning, we stumbled to our bedrooms. Kim paused just before opening her door.

"Miki, I'm here for you if you need me. But not right now, okay?"

"Yeah, Okay," I replied as I opened my door and fell into bed. *I remember thinking It might have been one of the best days of my life. Sure, the pancakes were delicious but my little sister was what made it special.* Kim's grown up, and we like each other!

Neither of us woke early on Sunday. We slept till noon, and by the time we got up, mom had cleaned the kitchen.

PART 4

From Hope to Healing

The Sunny Side of Crazy

CHAPTER 25
A LONG DARK DAY

It poured all day Sunday, which was perfect because I slept better when it rained. I was still too stuffed with pancakes to care about breakfast.

Last night my decision was made. I intended to walk into Dr. Manning's office Monday morning and declare! Decision made, I've decided to integrate! Of course, I knew it wouldn't be simple, but I felt strong enough to begin.

Today, I wasn't so sure. I wanted to talk to my secret friends and tell them how much I loved them and how I didn't want them to leave, but they had to go. In truth, I wanted their approval, permission and encouragement. In my heart, I knew it wouldn't happen.

Dr. Manning told me again and again, "Saying goodbye is not what integration is about." He talked in terms of aspects and attributes of my personality, but no matter how I looked at it, six (including me) becoming one, required goodbyes.

I flipped open my journal hoping to find some words there. Nothing, no new entries. I wondered if my alters knew I had to make the decision on my own.

Mom and I hadn't spoken more than a few words since our confrontation, and I needed to know if she'd go to the hypnosis session with me. So many times, I'd reminded her the sessions were none of her business. Now, not only was I going to be asking her to accompany me, but I needed her to.

187

The Sunny Side of Crazy

I got up, grabbed my robe, and headed to the kitchen where Mom was having tea and praising Kati on another excellent report card.

"Oh, Hi Miki, Why don't you have a cup of tea with us?" she said.

"Sounds good," I said, making my "let's make peace face" and flopping down on the chair next to my sister.

'No more for me," Kati said, as she quickly escaped from the room.

"Mom, Dr. Manning wants to talk to you."

Mom looked surprised. She'd learned not to pry and this obviously took her by surprise.

"Why does he want to see me?" she asked.

"He said if I decided to integrate, he'd hypnotize me. I asked if you could be with me."

Mom tried to hide the smile behind her eyes.

"You've decided?" she inquired.

"No, Mom, No! Not for sure. But, Dr. Manning said he'd need to talk to you about how to behave during a hypnosis session. He has ground rules for everything."

Mom completed her smile, nodded her head, and we finished our tea in silence.

CHAPTER 26
EXPECTATIONS, PREPARATION, REVELATIONS

When I returned to Dr. Manning's office after my diagnosis, I felt a strange excitement mixed with apprehension. The session was, to say the least, a letdown. After spending an exhausting weekend sorting through my past, I was eager to move on, but that's not what Dr. Manning had in mind!

"Good morning, Mikala, how was your weekend?" he said.

"Okay, I guess, I decided to integrate!"

Dr. Manning looked surprised. "You've made your decision rather quickly, haven't you? I thought we agreed to talk more about your diagnosis and the integration process today."

"If I wait, I might change my mind so let's go ahead."

"That's the reason I wanted you to take your time making your decision. You need to understand your disorder, what integration means. And be certain of what you want to do," he said.

"I've already thought about what it means —I won't be crazy anymore!"

I could tell by the look on his face, he wasn't happy with my flippant response.

" Oh, I'm sorry Dr. Manning, you don't like that word, do you? I'm tired of having a disorder. Is that better?" I backed down.

"Yes, as a matter of fact, it is," he stated.

"Sorry doctor," I blurted out.

Without responding to my apology, he asked what led to my decision.

I spent the rest of the session telling him about my weekend. I talked about my trunk, my baby pictures, the confrontation with Mom and my all-nighter with Kim. Before I knew it, our session was over.

"Mikala, it sounds like you had an exhausting and insightful weekend. I understand your eagerness to move forward, but we need to have a few sessions prior to the hypnosis session. I want to know your expectations are realistic and that you are prepared before we move to a hypnosis session."

Anxious, I cut him off. "Mom says she will come with me."

Dr. Manning smiled and started quietly tapping his pencil.

I felt good. Feeling hopeful felt good.

Our next couple of sessions were more like classes than therapy.

"Mikala, I think you need to know more about your disorder and the integration process. Would that be okay with you?" Dr. Manning asked.

"What do I need to know?" I asked.

The Sunny Side of Crazy

"Let's start with what Dissociative Identity Disorder is."

" I know what it is, Dr. Manning. I've lived with it for years. It means my secret friends have been in my head all along. You said I created them to protect myself, and when I go through hypnosis, I will find out why. Then, I don't know. I guess we'll talk about it. Right?"

"Right."

During the following sessions, we remained quiet for long periods of time. I needed that time to get my thoughts together.

"Dr. Manning, this might sound silly but I don't want my alters to die."

"I understand why you feel that way, Mikala, but remember, your alters are manifestations of yourself. They can't die," he explained.

"Mom says all people show different parts of themselves at different times and in different places," I said.

"What your mom said is true, but in your case, before you developed a strong individualized personality, something happened —something traumatic. Your mind couldn't handle it and created a team to get through it."

"A team that doesn't exist but feels so real," I added.

"They are all part of you, manifesting individually. You escape from reality from time to time and an alternative appears to take over. When that happens, there's a disconnect between your thoughts, identity, consciousness and memory," he continued.

"Whoa, Doctor, you're getting too techie for me. But I get what you are saying. That's why I forget so many things, isn't it? Sometimes I feel like whole pieces of my life are missing." I said.

"That's part of the disorder, Mikala. Each identity plays a different role. Over time, you've become pretty dependent on them. And, it's caused a loss of memory, as well as loss of control. When one loses control, their life becomes unmanageable." he said.

"To say the least!" I replied. "Dr. Manning, did you know I've been going to therapists on and off for over seven years and none of them ever told me this?"

"Sometimes the disorder is difficult to diagnose. It can be mistaken for schizophrenia because the patient is having delusions or hearing voices. Other times it can be diagnosed as borderline personality disorder. Symptoms overlap, and it takes time and experience for a therapist to recognize a patient has Dissociative Identity Disorder."

So what happens now?" I asked.

"That depends on you, Mikala. As I told you before you have options, you—" he said.

"I already know. I want to go ahead with the Integration process," I said emphatically.

"If that's what you have decided, I don't see any reason you can't successfully integrate," he said.

"So, does that mean hypnosis?" I asked.

The Sunny Side of Crazy

"Yes, but it also means accepting ownership of all your thoughts, feelings and experiences. It means taking responsibility for the different aspects of yourself, even the one you refer to as Tin the Terrible. It will require you to change your relationship with yourself and others, And Mikala, it means we will have to look at the role your alters played and what knowledge and skills you will need to acquire. We also have to look at what triggers switches, and you will have to learn to respond to them differently," he explained.

"About hypnosis, Dr. Manning?" When will it happen? I already told Mom she has to be with me."

Dr. Manning smiled, picked up his pencil, and before beginning to tap, said "You'll be the first to know, I promise."

Two weeks later, we were ready. It's hard to describe that fateful session. I was scared. No, to tell the truth, I was terrified! Dr. Manning recognized my fear the minute Mom and I walked into his office. Even as I laid down on his old plaid sofa, I could feel my heart pounding a mile a minute.

Dr. Manning's voice was soothing.

"Mikala, your mom and I are going to be right here with you, but if you are having second thoughts, we don't have to proceed with hypnosis today.

" No, Dr. Manning, I'm ready!" I replied, sounding more confident than I felt.

I began to relax as Dr. Manning's monotone voice began to guide me down a long hallway. I took a few steps and stopped in front of the fourth door. I stared at the number; hesitantly, then opened the door and walked in.

Suddenly a flashback; I was a terrified four-year-old listening to a creaking door and watching a dark shadow come closer and closer to my bed. I tried to scream but no sounds came out. I closed my eyes tight hoping the shadow would go away. It didn't. I felt pain and cried out for my mother. Then, I saw her. She was there, she knew what was happening but didn't help me!

I was reliving the trauma that left me physically and mentally scarred for my entire life. I was experiencing what I would never be able to deny or forget. It was painful. It was heartbreaking. Why wouldn't my mother help me?

A gentle, soothing voice was calling my name. It started as a whisper and grew louder and louder. "You're okay, Mikala, You're safe now, You're okay."

I opened my eyes. Mom was sitting in a chair across the room, tears running down her face.

Dr. Manning and I didn't talk during that session. It was time to grieve. The time to process began the following week. Healing then began.

Two years later, I was still seeing Dr. Manning. And, eventually, I didn't need regular sessions very often at all. I had become me.

A couple of months ago, Mom asked if I missed my alters, and I told her, honestly, they will always be important memories. But, I like being my own person. I've found I can live without them. I feel complete. My puzzle pieces have been put together, and I like how everything turned out.

CHAPTER 27
THROUGH A MOTHER'S EYES

The day after the hypnosis session, Mikala and I talked for a very long time. She no longer asked why her mother gave her away. She asked other questions, questions no mother wants to hear. "Why did it happen to me? Why? My mother knew. Why didn't she stop him?"

I had no answers. "It wasn't your fault" was all I could come up with and that certainly wasn't enough. I hoped and prayed Dr. Manning could erase the pain I saw in her eyes. And, over time, he did.

Mikala continued to see Dr. Manning and chose to keep their sessions private. I learned not to pry but I saw changes; changes I thought I might never see. Mikala developed a vibrant personality of her own. One that incorporated aspects of her secret friends.

She is no longer excessively self-involved. She shows compassion and concern for the less fortunate and volunteers to work with several local non-profits agencies. Her world has opened up and she loves reading about the people and places around her.

Learning to laugh at herself was a milestone. One evening she was singing Happy Birthday off-key. We all laughed when she said. "OMG, I used to think I could be an opera singer. What in the world was I thinking?"

The Sunny Side of Crazy

Today, Mikala remains a casual girl. Sophistication isn't her style but being a know-it-all still is. No doubt, that was Skye's gift to her. Now and then, we see a trace of Tin. But it comes in a flash and passes almost as quickly. We no longer walk on eggshells.

Mikala's story isn't a fairy tale and integration wasn't a magic cure. It took years of therapy to unravel Mikala's complicated life. Working to rebuild it was difficult. There were many boulders to climb, tears to shed, and roads to travel. Each step provided clues to the next. It's a process that continues even today.

I often wonder if anything would have been different if I had known about her disorder before she became an adult. I'll never know. But, just as the water bearer said at the beginning of this story, without his pot being just the way it was, he would not have had such beauty to grace his house. Without Mikala being just the way was, we would not have had so much beauty in ours.

So, what does the future hold? Who knows? Most likely, more boulders to climb, tears to shed, and roads to travel but we'll always be there for each other.

The End

GLOSSARY

Dissociative Identity Order (DID)

Previously known as Multiple Personalities, Dissociative Identity Disorder is a mental disorder characterized by the maintenance of at least two distinct and relatively enduring personality states.

DID is included in the Diagnostic and Statistical Manual and remains among the most controversial of disorders in the psychiatry and legal system.

Integration

The integration process focuses on addressing the safety of the patient, managing exposure to, and the processing of the hidden original traumatic event(s), as well as the integration of alter identities into one complete personality.

Characters

Michiko

The original name of little Mikala

Mikala

The child with Dissociative Identity Disorder

Mikala's alters

Sam	Shy, sensitive, loving, and caring
Suki	Proper, curious, loves learning and teaching
Calle	Bubbly, an outgoing, prankster, loves attention
Skye	Sophisticated, sexy, dramatic, talented, fearless
Tin	Angry, dangerous, with rare sudden appearances

Dissociative Identity Disorder
Entertainment
or
Education?

For years, the film industry has used Dissociative Identity Disorder aka. Multiple Personalities as a profitable way to entertain audiences with gory, gruesome and creepy thrillers.

Films with names like Psycho, Primal Fear, Secret Window and Shutter Island, among others, have portrayed characters with multiple personalities as serial killers, predators, and the demonically possessed.

Unfortunately, sitting on the edge of one's seat in a dark room, watching the big screen is the worst way to learn about a subject that deserves serious study and respect.

I would encourage readers to reference information about Dissociative Identity Disorder available on The National Association on Mental Illness website.

The Sunny Side of Crazy

ABOUT THE AUTHOR

Tricia Mikouchi is a writer, speaker, and life coach living on the East Coast with four daughters, three grandchildren, and two demanding dogs. Although The Sunny Side of Crazy is her first publication, there are more to follow in 2022.

For more information about Tricia Mikouchi or to book her as a speaker or life coach, please contact her at:

pmikouchi@gmail.com

Also available as an e-Book

CPSIA information can be obtained
at www.ICGtesting.com
Printed in the USA
LVHW010834070422
715428LV00008B/85